A BETTER PROVISION
FIFTY YEARS ON

Hazel Harvey

4th July 1998

DEAN ALURED CLARKE SAID OF THE WINCHESTER HOSPITAL,
'Whenever a better provision is made for the sick poor by Parliament, this hospital will cease, or become part of that provision.'

The Royal Devon & Exeter Hospital 1948-1998

A BETTER PROVISION
FIFTY YEARS ON

HAZEL HARVEY

FOREWORD BY
Professor Ruth Hawker OBE

HALSGROVE

Royal Devon and Exeter Healthcare NHS Trust
Exeter 1998

© Royal Devon and Exeter Healthcare NHS Trust 1998

First published in 1998

ISBN 1-898386-32-3
Edited and produced by
Delian Bower Publishing
Exeter, England

Designed by Vic Giolitto

Distributed by
Halsgrove, Lower Moor Way, Tiverton, Devon EX16 6SS

Printed and bound by
SRP Exeter

CONTENTS

FOREWORD

I am delighted to be able to introduce this history of the Royal Devon & Exeter Hospital as we celebrate 50 years of the NHS. Pat Russell told the story up to 1948 in his very fine *A History of the Exeter Hospitals* and the final paragraph of his introduction clearly marks the end of an era:

The narrative ends on the 'Appointed Day' (5 July 1948) when the National Health Service was inaugurated, and the responsibility for all hospitals, unless specifically exempt, was vested in the Minister of Health. Apart from the continued activities of loyal Friends of Hospitals it marked the end of the voluntary system.

It was considered fitting by the Board of the present Royal Devon and Exeter Healthcare NHS Trust to commission 'the story' of the last 50 years, during which time a new building, started in the 1960s to replace the hospital first developed at Southernhay was itself replaced by another new building, opened in 1992.

The Royal Devon & Exeter Hospital, or 'RD&E' as it is widely known to staff and patients, features in many people's lives. Hundreds of thousands of patients have passed through the doors for a whole range of reasons in the last 50 years, and large numbers of staff have been employed in various capacities to continue to provide high quality patient care. All will have their own memories and their own stories to tell.

This account is based on the recollections of people who have been involved in the hospital during part of this period. The Trust is grateful to the many people who agreed to be interviewed and share their experiences. Many quotes and short character sketches are skilfully woven into this history by Hazel Harvey. There inevitably are omissions; this does not in any way devalue the contribution made by each individual member of staff not named, but some selection was unavoidable.

I believe staff who have worked, or still work, at the RD&E will enjoy this book, as will many Devonians and Exonians who have received care at the RD&E and its associated hospitals, as well as those interested in local history or the history of healthcare.

Throughout their history the Hospitals, incorporated since April 1993 as the RD&E Trust, have endeavoured, as 'Institutions of Care', to serve the community of which they are a part.

This history is only part of that story but will serve as a record of achievement in five decades of major social change.

Professor Ruth Hawker OBE
Chairman
RD&E Healthcare NHS Trust

INTRODUCTION

On 5 July 1948 the hospitals of Exeter were nationalized and taken into the new national health service. This brought under one yoke institutions of widely different origins and different reputations. The Royal Devon & Exeter (RD&E) Hospital in Southernhay was more than 200 years old, one of the oldest provincial voluntary-funded hospitals in England. The City Hospital on Heavitree Road was regarded affectionately as the place where many new Exonians came into the world, and older ones were cared for, but without forgetting that it had once been the municipal workhouse. The West of England Eye Infirmary (WEEI) was the oldest provincial eye hospital in England, and the Princess Elizabeth Orthopaedic Hospital (PEOH) had an equally proud history.

However, anyone who thought that nationalization would bring uniformity and loss of identity need not have worried. The tale of the first fifty years of the National Health Service (NHS) in Exeter is as full of unique incidents, pioneering achievements and dramatic events as anything in the preceding centuries. The Devon and Exeter Hospital in Southernhay, founded in 1741, has been described as the first purpose-built district general hospital in England. By the 1940s, therefore, the state of its accommodation put it high on the list for rebuilding. After countless delays the out-of-town replacement came into use in 1974, only to be diagnosed with 'concrete cancer' just ten years later. Exeter then had the unique experience of having to build a second new hospital only a few years after the first. The good news was that design could be improved, and the latest therapies accommodated. And now, at the end of the 1990s, the new hospital is bringing together on one site all the main institutions involved in this story: Southernhay, City, West of England Eye Infirmary and Princess Elizabeth Orthopaedic Hospital.

CHAPTER ONE

'Blessings for the County of Devon and its Metropolis'
THE HOSPITAL'S FOUNDATION AND FIRST TWO CENTURIES

Dr Alured Clarke,
Dean of Exeter, portrayed
by the Revd James Wills.

To put the last fifty years into perspective we need a brief history of healthcare in Exeter during the previous centuries. When the monasteries were closed down in the 1540s, their physick gardens and hospices were also lost. For the next two centuries the sick could not expect any public care. From the 1670s Exeter's destitute could find shelter in the workhouse on the east bank of the Chute brook at the foot of Paris Street. The rich could afford to send for a doctor and hire a nurse, but the majority fell between these two extremes. They had to depend on folk remedies, quack doctors and the kindness of family and neighbours.

Towards the middle of the eighteenth century the new concept of 'voluntary hospitals' was seen as the way to help the sick poor, to funnel the charitable impulse more effectively than merely carrying soup to cottagers. The invalid could be offered rest and perhaps a cure. The doctors could practise on a steady supply of cases. They would gladly give their services free, knowing that the honorary attachment to a hospital would enhance their reputations so that they could charge their private patients more.

Dr Alured Clarke was appointed Dean of Exeter Cathedral in January 1740/1.* He had established a Voluntary Hospital in Winchester in 1736, and although he himself was not well,

*What we would call 1741 but regarded then as still in 1740. Before 1752 each year ran on until 25 March.

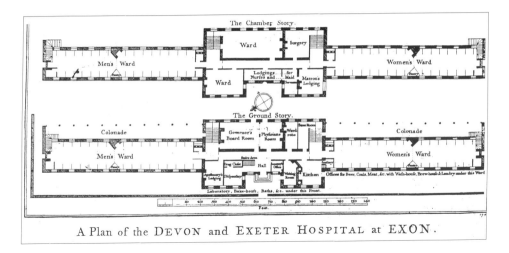

A Plan of the DEVON and EXETER HOSPITAL at EXON.

indeed was to die aged 46 on 3 May 1742, he was determined 'not to give sleep to his eyes nor slumber to his eyelids, until he had secured the same blessings for the County of Devon and its Metropolis.'

Dean Clarke's wish became reality with such incredible speed that part of the hospital was up and equipped to admit patients by 1 January 1742/3. The Dean held the first meeting of Subscribers in the Cathedral Chapter House on 23 July 1741. The site was offered on 6 August. The builder had prepared the plan by 27 August when the foundation stone was laid, little more than a month from the launch. Sites had been inspected in both Northernhay and Southernhay, equally elevated and airy, equally 'out-of-town' (being outside the city walls). Southernhay was virtually undeveloped. It was still used for horse fairs and the annual Lammas Fair. (The Georgian terraces on either side were not built until 1795–1824). John Tuckfield (future Tory MP for Exeter) provided the plot, facing Trinity Burial Ground and the wall of the Bishop's Palace. County gentry donated cartloads of timber, sand, stone and slate. A local builder, John Richards, gave his services free, offering to design the hospital and supervise its erection. It was to be 'as plain and frugal as possible' and indeed the only decora-

Dated 1741, this is probably John Richard's first hurried plan produced for fund-raising. It shows partitions marking the site of each bed. The wings are not staggered as they will be when built.

tions are the rusticated quoins, dentil band under the eaves, and central cupola. The roof is hipped and covered with large slates. It still graces Southernhay 250 years later, whilst its 1970s replacement has had to be demolished after less than 25 years.

The site slopes, so the cellars are below street level but not underground. The basement of the central block housed Laboratory, Bake-house and Baths. The South Wing cellars held the Wash-house, Brew-house, Laundry, and stores for coal and provisions.

In the ground floor of the main block was an elegantly proportioned Board Room where the Governors met every Thursday. It would benefit from many legacies over the years, which added Chippendale chairs and panelling and a growing collection of portraits of benefactors and eminent doctors, by equally eminent artists.

In September 1741 the Dean sent an appeal to every church and chapel in Devon. Every subscriber or contributing congregation would be entitled to recommend one patient at a time. The target was £3,000, which would help two thousand of Devon's sick poor every

Etching of 1809 after W. Davey. The central recess had been brought forward and topped with a pediment in 1772. Some windows are still blocked up after the window-tax of 1747 exacted a shilling per window over nineteen.

year. 160 beds would accommodate 1,000 patients a year with lodging, diet, advice and medicine. A similar number of so-called 'Out-Patients' would have just the advice and medicine, but also gratis. Dean Clarke's adviser on the medical arrangements was Dr Michael Lee Dicker. Also in September 1741 the Governors approved Dicker's election as Physician, together with five others (Drs Andrew, Bent, Glass, Hallett and Walrond) and five Surgeons (Messrs Parr, Patch Sr and Jr, Pillett and Walker). In attracting doctors, the County was in competition with the City, for the Guardians of the Poor had a rival scheme for a hospital in the old workhouse. (A new workhouse had been built in 1699–1707 higher up the Heavitree Road). The City did open a hospital with 40 beds a few months before the one in Southernhay but it closed from lack of funds in 1754.

The Devon and Exeter Hospital fared better. A matron and two nurses were appointed before it opened. They were joined in February by a resident Apothecary, who was instructed to do a daily ward round and to remain on call at all times. The Statutes also required:

That the Clergy of Exeter be desired to attend, by Weekly Rotation, to visit the Sick, and to read Prayers every Day in the Wards, and to give the Communion at proper times.

The category of persons who could be helped was strictly controlled:

No Children under seven Years of Age; No Woman big with Child; no Person disordered in their Senses, or suspected to have the Small-Pox, Itch, or any other infectious Disease; nor any that are apprehended to be in a consumptive, or dying condition ...

That certainly made for a better success rate.

There were thirty beds to start with, arranged sideways along the walls, feet meeting at the centre of each window but divided by partitions. Patients were admitted on Thursdays. The rules were read out to them on Friday morning. Rule Six may have come as a shock to anyone looking forward to a rest:

That such of the Patients, as are able to work, do assist the Nurses and other Servants, in nursing the Patients, washing and ironing the Linnen, washing and cleaning the Wards; and in doing such other Business as the Matron shall require.

Until 1815, when mains water was brought in, patients had to take shifts pumping water from the well in the basement to the cistern in the roof. Matron herself was to call the register

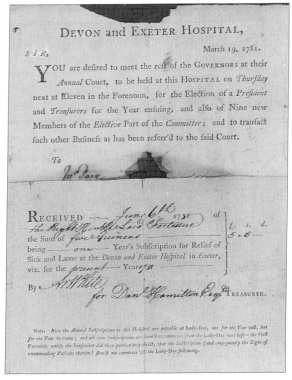

Invitation to the AGM of 1781 and receipt for a subscription
of the same year.

morning and evening in each ward, and lock the gates at night.

Rule Seventeen for In-Patients stated:

That when the Patients are cured, they be enjoined by the Chairman to return thanks to ALMIGHTY GOD in their respective place of publick Worship.

Of the Rules for Out-Patients, the first was 'That they attend exactly at the Time appointed by the Apothecary.' The possibility of waiting-lists was foreseen:

Provision is made by the Rules of the Hospital, that they can never stay more than a Week before they are received into the House, if all the Beds should happen to be full at the Time of their coming.

Annual expenditure in the first ten years averaged £608 (wages, provisions, candles, coal – and trees and plants for the physick garden). In the yard pigs ate the leftovers and provided protein for the kitchen, until they were declared a health hazard in 1793.

The North Wing was completed in 1748. The earliest wards, in the South Wing and the central block, had been named Devon, Exeter, Bristol and Winchester. Later additions were also named after relevant places: Gloucester, Plymouth, the Cornish Ward, Northampton, Bath, Somerset, London. In 1756 an operating theatre, a casualty department and surgical wards were added. By then the staff consisted of the apothecary, matron, secretary, eight nurses, cook, housemaid, laundrymaid and porter/messenger. From the start the Exeter doctors were at the forefront of medical practice. John Patch Sr was

An etching illustrating a description of the Hospital in Besley's Guide of 1836. The pavement is noticeably better surfaced than the carriageway.

the first surgeon in the West Country to remove stones from the bladder. Bartholomew Parr, 54 years a surgeon at the hospital, was a skilled obstetrician. Dr Thomas Glass developed the treatment of 'continual fevers' and 'miliary fever'. He also pioneered the therapeutic use of baths, and was concerned about the dangers of smallpox inoculation. (From 1807 the safer cowpox inoculation would be offered free on Tuesdays and Wednesdays). John Blackall's book on dropsy (1813) anticipated Bright. Many Devonians were being cured of longstanding complaints. Funds continued to flow into the strongbox. (Exeter had no banks until 1769).

In 1780 an extra dozen beds were provided and it was minuted by the Governors that:

it is detrimental both to the interest and the credit of the Hospital to put two patients in one bed, and it be recommended by this Court to the Committee to put an entire stop to the practice.

In the same year it was agreed that:

a leaping-stock or upping-block be erected near the entrance for the better accommodation of country patients in alighting from and remounting their horses.

In September 1789 the manager of the Bedford Circus Theatre handed in £30 from a benefit performance by Mrs Sarah Siddons.

But in June 1796 there came the first cash crisis. Five wards had to close for several months, leaving only 43 beds in use. One ward reopened in 1798, one in 1799, but there followed two bad harvests, and 64 beds were taken out of service in 1805. The Board of Governors stated that they entertained:

too high an opinion of the wisdom and humanity of the Nobility, Gentry, Clergy and Yeomanry of the County of Devon and its Neighbourhood to think for a moment that they will suffer to sink into decay an Establishment which has restored to health 41,500 of our indigent fellow creatures ...

In 1808 an eye hospital with six beds opened in Holloway Street, moving in 1813 to Magdalen Street. Its first oculists, John Saunders and William Adams, had been pupils of the same Barnstaple GP before studying at Guy's and St Thomas's hospitals. Saunders founded Moorfields in 1804 and taught the new method of removing cataracts there. He then helped Adams set up the

Dr Thomas Shapter portrayed in 1847 by John Prescott Knight, physician at the Hospital 1847–77. He arrived in Exeter in the year of the cholera epidemic and published a detailed account of it.

Exeter hospital. A notable early success was the gift of sight to a thirty-year-old who had been born blind. 28 cataract cases were cured in the first year. Patients were admitted for stays of up to ten weeks. This 'West of England Eye Infirmary' was financed by subscriptions and donations, but any clergyman – subscriber or not – could send a poor parishioner for free treatment. 'The recommendation to this establishment is a bad eye.'

One Thursday in July 1809 an actor, Joseph Wilde, who had torn a knee ligament performing in pantomime at Devonport, was admitted to the Southernhay hospital for rest. He com-

posed a long poem expressing gratitude to

This hospital, this noble monument
of human worth;
Where now I lie, struck by the awful
hand of Providence,
To punish my mistreadings …

On his first morning in the ward he was amazed to see Rule Six in action:

All who can wield an instrument
of labour,
Are busily employed on cleanliness;
Till the whole ward,
for neatness might compare
And wholesome sweetness,
with a monarch's palace.

By then the Apothecary and individual physicians and surgeons in Southernhay were taking on paying apprentices. One of many excellent teachers was the notable anatomist John Sheldon, appointed to the hospital staff in 1797. In 1819 two of Sheldon's pupils,

Home-brewed beer was the nourishing, germ-free staple beverage. The gardener Ambrose Holms supplied vegetables and medicinal herbs. John Folland was brewer to the hospital for 50 years; he wore a grey uniform trimmed with scarlet. Matron took charge of the keys to the brewhouse at 9 pm each evening.

Mr John Harris, surgeon at the hospital 1815–55, drew this view of it from Mount Radford in 1852, just before the Halford extension. The tree-filled Chute valley had a century to wait before the inner by-pass viaduct replaced it.

Arthur Kempe's chapel, architect John Hayward, capacity 150, licensed in July 1869. Kempe paid one tenth of his income to charity.

John Haddy James (after serving as a surgeon at Waterloo) and Samuel Barnes, began giving anatomy classes which attracted students from all over Devon and Cornwall. A properly organized medical school developed and flourished until 1858. (A Medical Act of that year put a stop to provincial medical schools. Thereafter, doctors at the Devon and Exeter reverted to the old

Top & above: Bowring Ward for children.

Left: Matron orders potatoes in 1886.

Below: Southernhay frontage showing Chapel and Hospital.

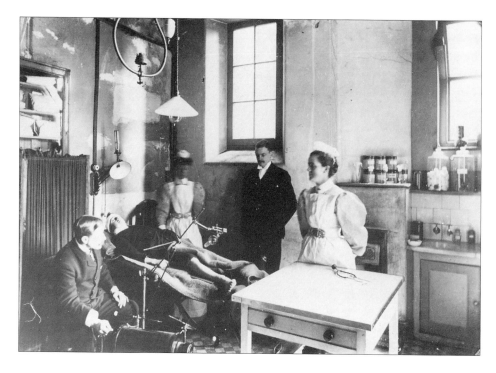

Early use of X-ray on a leg. An induction coil is pepping up the voltage of a tiny Coolidge/cathode tube. The surgeon may be Russell Coombe.

system of taking on individual pupils. This continued until the 1890s).

In 1821 beds were arranged feet to the wall instead of sideways on. Four years later they tried head to the wall, and this has remained the accepted practice. In 1828 Haddy James pioneered the use of weights and pulleys to apply safe traction to a broken femur. In 1848 he introduced the use of a sucker on the baby's head during delivery. He was also a founder member of the British Medical Association.

In 1832 Exeter was ravaged by cholera. When the hospital staff began to fall ill the laundry room and carpenter's shop became emergency isolation wards.

At about this time surgeons were beginning to have misgivings about leaving post-operative patients in the hands of kindly but untrained nurses. In 1835 a special 'operations' nurse was appointed to care for them.

Cathedral services were held on each anniversary of the Dean's foundation, with the collection going towards repair of the hospital. In 1836 a larger sum than usual was needed, and ladies in pretty hats were mustered to take the collection plates round, to good effect. Until 1847 the Apothecary was the resident in charge of the patients. In that year the post was changed to one of House Surgeon. In 1852 a vast legacy of over £70,000 from Mrs Halford, daughter of Mr Cresswell of New Court, solved the financial problems, indeed paid for a new multi-storey wing, with gas lighting, sanitary facilities and a modern kitchen. During the Crimean War a Scotswoman asked to train here before joining Florence Nightingale at Scutari. She was allowed to help for the month of June 1855. Ten years later the hospital began a proper training scheme for pupil nurses. A surgeon at the hospital, William Budd, was far ahead of his time when he declared in 1856 that typhoid was spread by faecal contamination of water and milk. Ward names now commemorated benefactors: Dean Clarke,

Tuckfield, Cresswell, Rolle. Rolle was formerly 'Somerset' and in 1860 became 'Bowring' when a legacy from Sir John Bowring was used to adapt one ward for children, 'to relieve the general wards of wailing children and disturbed nights.' A chapel was added in 1868–9 at the expense of one of the surgeons, Arthur Kempe (who also provided the Fountain in Exeter at the top of Sidwell Street). The chapel was Victorian Gothic in style with a frontage on Southernhay. It played a central part in life at the hospital. Photographs of some of its stained-glass windows are displayed in the lobby of the present chapel at the RD&E, together with one of the six sanctuary lamps, converted from gas to electricity.

Matron was still nominally in overall command of the tired nurses, rebellious patients and unrestricted numbers of visitors. The House Surgeon reported in 1871 'that almost all the entire work of the hospital is at present done by the patients … to their serious hurt.'

Mrs Halford's legacy kept the hospital in funds until 1874, when the Bishop had

Nurses in their recreation room but still in caps and aprons while relaxing.

to be asked to reinstitute appeals to all of Devon's Sunday congregations. After the terrible fire at the Theatre Royal in 1887 most of the 200 injured were taken to the hospital, which was later allocated £250 from the Disaster Fund.

Exeter doctors continued to remain abreast, or slightly ahead, of the latest developments. In 1872 a new surgeon, Mr Roper, surprised everyone by washing his hands before operating. Cocaine drops were used as a local anaesthetic for cataract surgery on 29 November 1884, only ten weeks after this practice had been discussed in Heidelberg. An X-ray was used in Southernhay as early as 1898.

In 1888 the Nursing Sub-Committee agreed that the training and living conditions of the nurses were unsatisfactory. They were no longer to sleep in cubicles on the wards but have a bedroom each in a Nurses' Home, their own dining-room and a recreation room. Enough full-time nurses were to be

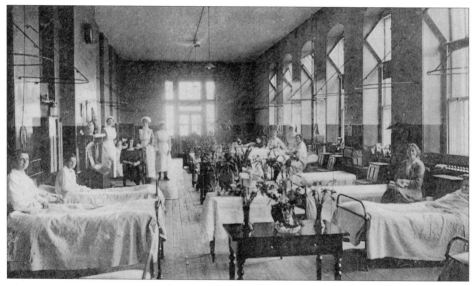

Above: Newcourt Ward (Female Medical).   Below: Dean Clarke Ward (Male Medical).

employed to cover night duty rather than relying on moonlighting charwomen and washerwomen. This decision coincided with a major reorganization of all the accommodation. The original wards from 1741 could not be brought up to modern standards – they became offices. New kitchens were built upstairs. Another large wing was added, and named Victoria by the Duke and Duchess of York in 1899. After their visit, Queen Victoria consented to a request that the hospital's name become 'The Royal Devon and Exeter'. The

Albert Memorial Museum was also visited and granted the same distinction.

So Exeter began the twentieth century with its voluntary hospital proudly 'royal', and young moustachioed doctors driving to work along Southernhay in their 'growlers' and pony carts. Fundraising continued, with flag days and special collections and appeals for legacies and gifts. An ominous new note was sounded in 1907 when a London driver sent £5 towards the treatment of a woman he had knocked down in St Thomas. The Eye Infirmary moved to

The Board Room in Southernhay, where the Governors convened, patients were interviewed before admission or discharge, and the staff entered only for their retirement presentations.

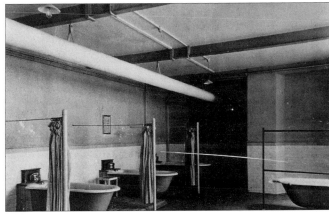

Baths in the basement at Southernhay.

greatly enlarged premises above Bull Meadow in 1901, during Miss Georgina Kinninmont's 16 years as matron there.

On Heavitree Road a new 150-bed Infirmary block for the workhouse was built in 1905. It was still run by the Guardians of the Poor of the City and County of Exeter, and still funded by local rates. The inscription on the foundation stone reads 'Lord behold he whom thou lovest is sick.' J.A.W. Pereira came to Exeter to serve as the infirmary doctor. He later added 'Gray' to his name and passed it down to several

generations of distinguished Exeter doctors, a veritable dynasty, comparable to those of Patch, Parr and Budd in earlier centuries.

The First World War brought black-out and temporary emergency use of the Eye Infirmary. The royal Yorks, now George V and Queen Mary, visited the war-wounded there, travelling from the railway station this time by motor. Voluntary Aid nurses trained at the RD&E. In 1918 the king granted the hospital the right to display the royal coat of arms.

Problems after the war were the long

Alderman Vincent Thompson, of whom Sir Edgar Plummer said he did not know any man who more enjoyed spending money for the benefit of others, was on the RD&E House Committee 1918–50, was the last President of the independent hospital in 1948 and the first Chair of the NHS Committee. He was also chair of the Devon & Exeter Cancer Fund.

waiting-lists for tonsil and adenoid cases, the flu epidemic, long-stay cases (especially disabled soldiers and TB) and malaria and VD brought home by the troops. Disabled soldiers were nursed temporarily in Streatham Hall, the Bishop's Palace and other places, until the Victory Ward was ready for them in 1922, along the Magdalen Street edge of the hospital's grounds, with accommodation for nurses upstairs. By now X-rays were used routinely, and cancer was being treated with radium. A new so-called Electrical Department was opened in the Halford Wing in 1925. The Devon & Exeter Cancer Fund, founded in 1923, gave £1,000-worth of radium, and further apparatus and more radium as it was needed.

The Devonian Cripples Care Association under the chairmanship of Dame Georgiana Buller acquired the Veitch nursery ground at Buckerell Bore and built a hospital for 48 children. Exeter Rotary Club raised £2,500 towards the cost of one wing including operating theatre and equipment. The hospital was opened by the current Duke and Duchess of York in November 1927. They suggested that it should be named after their little daughter, the Princess Elizabeth. It was the first institution in the country to receive this honour. In July 1933 an extension providing wards for adults and babies was inaugurated by Princess Alice, Countess of Athlone. The aim of the hospital was to detect and quickly treat such crippling diseases as tubercular joints, rickets, osteomyelitis and polio. The single-

Matron Stopford-Smyth 1929-49.

Staff of the West of England Eye Infirmary, possibly on Ransom Pickard's retirement in 1932. Pickard central, then Miss Penny (matron 1906–36) and G. P. D. Hawker. At the back the diminutive Dr R. Fortescue Foulkes. The others could be F. Roper (of a dynasty of Exeter doctors), P. D. Warburton (died 1938) and M. Dykes Bower (appointed 1932).

storey buildings were of light construction, designed to last only 30 years. Rosemary Sutcliff, the author of outstanding historical novels, had many operations here as a child. Her autobiography, *Blue Remembered Hills*, describes Girl Guide activities, the painful treatments, and wards that were so healthily airy that they had neither walls nor ceilings, just an open roof sheltering gas heaters that were lit with a taper.

In 1930 the Poor Law Guardians were disbanded. The Workhouse Infirmary became the City Hospital, run by the council. It continued to cater for normal maternity cases, and to shelter the aged and chronic sick.

Harry Bazley, visiting his wife in the RD&E in 1930, was offered the job of boilerman, looking after two massive coal-fired boilers producing 12,000 lb of steam per hour. He never missed a day's work in the following 33 years. The job included incineration of amputated limbs until the boilers were converted to oil in 1955.

From 1927 working men had been able to contribute to the new Exeter Hospital Aid Society, which paid the hospital about thirty shillings a week

when a member was admitted. President Rowsell pointed out that it was founded solely to benefit the RD&E and the hospital had done the right thing by adopting it as its official scheme. 'West of England people are pretty clannish and they do like their own thing – when they understand it.' It made a vital contribution towards balancing the books at the RD&E where expenditure in 1932 was £3,373 but there was still an annual deficit of about £2,000. Road accidents were an increasing financial burden. In 1935 161 casualties were treated, and an additional 107 cases had to be admitted. 'Hospital Motor Week' had been held annually since 1925. By 1936 Sir Edgar Plummer reckoned that there were 50,000 licensed drivers in the area. They were asked to buy and display half-crown and five-shilling 'stamps'. Miss Alexandra

Stopford-Smyth, matron 1929–49, persuaded the committee that a new Nurses' Home was needed, and one was put up behind matron's house and opened in 1932. It had a croquet lawn at the rear. The Home was strategically placed – matron could see 'all the comings and goings.' Edward VIII was prevailed upon to send £250 to endow one of the nurses' bedrooms. Another money-spinning device was Hospital Pound Day – tour the hospital and give a pound of tea, butter or '… perhaps even a paper pound.' Sir Edgar, president for 14 years – 'the Plummer Years' – also made the usual Easter appeals for eggs. These regularly brought in enough to last the year, 60–70,000 all at once, collected in the villages ('Careful, dear, when you wake up – there's eggs on the stairs') – and laid in isinglass in the basement. Plummer also launched a straightforward appeal for cash to build the new Outpatients Department, and £36,000 rolled in. But in a typically convoluted appeal to novelty and local sentiment, people were invited to mark its opening in 1937 by presenting apple 'purses' containing £5 notes. The apples were of a variety named after Alderman Charles Ross of Exeter and were provided from Ronald Whiteway's cider orchards. Enough extra was raised to install wireless reception in the wards, and a telephone system with luminous indicators.

As the Nazi threat built up, the voluntary hospital system was increasingly seen as thoroughly English, the opposite of Hitler's tyrannical state control. The Odeon cinema, built from all-British materials, opened on 30 August 1937 with a fund-raising showing of an all-British film, The Charge of the Light Brigade. Sir Edgar Plummer spoke against the idea of nationalizing the hospitals. They would not be run so economically, would lose the goodwill of thousands of people, would lose millions in subscriptions and would lose the services of their honorary medical staff.

The medical staff were still few in number. In 1939 the 280 beds at the RD&E were served by two physicians, two surgeons, one pathologist, two anaesthetists and one 'MO i/c Electrical Treatment Department'. One of the honorary physicians, Charles Seward, born in Melbourne in 1898, had been appointed in 1929. He set up home in William Budd's former house, 20 Southernhay West. General medicine in the provinces embraced paediatrics, neurology and dermatology, but Seward was also especially interested in gastroenterology and diabetes, and handled psychosomatic disorders with understanding. While serving in the RAMC in India in 1942–5 he worked up his notes from his clinical experience in Exeter to form the basis of his best-selling Bedside Diagnosis (1949). This was based on the concept of disease as a disturbance of function. It classified the causes of disease according to the symptoms and signs they produced. It ran to twelve updated editions in 36 years and was translated into five European languages. Seward was at sea when Hitler raided Exeter, but his wife and children sheltered safely in the winecellar while twelve ceilings came down upstairs. Clifford James Fuller, who had been born in Mauritius and wounded on the Somme, was also appointed as a physician in 1929 but had to be treated for TB in Switzerland before taking up his position here. He made a special study of 'Farmer's Lung'.

The 'Electrical Department' embraced both radiotherapy and diagnostic radiology. Charles Wroth was the RD&E's senior consultant radiologist and ran both parts until 1947. The 1942 blitz destroyed Wroth's house and all his equipment. Mr Wayland Smith, a surgeon at the hospital from 1920, also had his Southernhay consulting-room destroyed. The pathologist since 1931 had been Dr Austin Robb, supported by one technician.

Three appointments were made in 1934: Norman Lock as Hon. Surgeon, Alan Gairdner as Hon. Asst. Surgeon, and Norman Capener as Hon. Orthopaedic Surgeon.

In April 1938 a salmon 2ft 6 ins long had leapt into a canoe near Exe Bridge and two surprised young men brought it to the hospital as a gift. The RD&E was still regarded as a charity, helping the impoverished classes. The comfortably off were supposed to use nursing homes. Murray French (later chair of Exeter & Mid Devon Health Authority) recalls that his father was taken into the RD&E with a broken leg in 1939, as 'the first casualty of war', when his Home Guard unit reacted to a false alarm that the Germans were coming, and he fell over a wall in the blackout. He was very conscious of the fact that his father was a Subscriber, someone who issued Recommends. He was so embarrassed at receiving free treatment that he gave £100 to the hospital on leaving.

At the bicentenary celebration in the Cathedral on 27 July 1941, Bishop Charles Curzon said that the hospital embodied democracy, local pride and local effort. Something very precious would be lost if it were swallowed up by the State. In the Second World War students of the Royal Free Hospital were evacuated to the University College of the South West, and attended the RD&E for clinical instruction. Charles Wroth accepted five students for training as radiographers in October 1940. Radium worth £5000 bought by the Devon Cancer Fund was buried for safety under the west wing. The hospital committee advertised that they would be grateful if Market Gardeners, Allotment Holders and Householders would kindly send their surplus Vegetables for the Patients. Residents in the Copplestone district sent in three tons of potatoes, nine cwt of turnips and other useful vegetables.

Then came the blitz of 4 May 1942.

The City Hospital suffered direct hits which killed 18 patients, destroyed many of its buildings and burnt all its records. The RD&E escaped major damage, but not the terror of bombs falling all around and fires raging. Incendiary bombs on the roof, and one which penetrated the basement stores, were quickly put out by the ARP warden, the porter and terrified young nurses, who then rushed to evacuate the upstairs wards to the basement corridor. A letter home from a nineteen-year-old student nurse, Betty Biggs, reassured her family that she had survived:

The bombs came whistling down and blew the blackout down and the windows and doors off their hinges … and the children started to cry … A strong wind was blowing. The dive bombing and machine-gunning were dreadful … the sky was scarlet with fires … Burnt and bleeding casualties were brought in … Fires raged mountain high all round, fire brigades all chasing up and down the street and the place was swimming with water and mud.

When she finally went to her room she found it had lost half a wall and there was broken glass, bricks and dirt everywhere. For a week the nurses hardly had a chance to sleep, and no time to change out of their uniforms.

Matron Stopford-Smyth was on duty all hours. Secretary John Sullivan worked for three days non-stop.

The war dragged on. Beryl Raphael began a nine-month pre-nursing course in 1943 and found it was more like domestic service, cleaning saucepans, making forty junkets every morning for poorly people, and summoning up all her courage when a huge pike was donated for her to gut. The porter had a bedroom above his cubby-hole by the main entrance. Doctors and matron

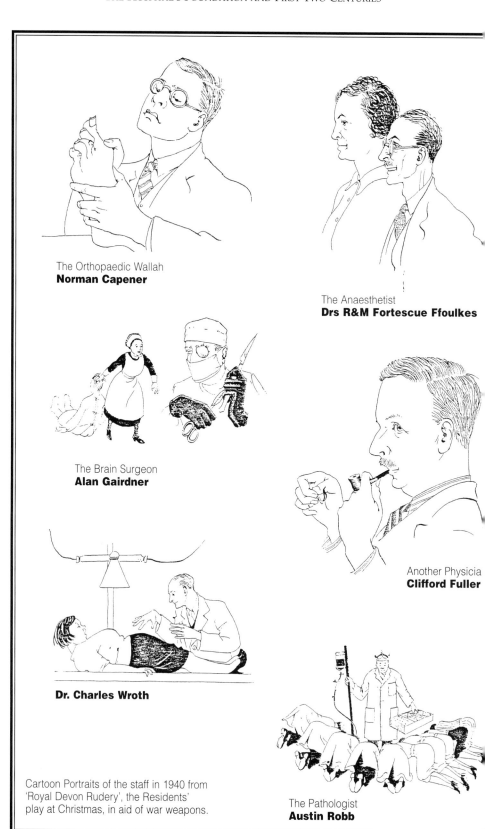

The Orthopaedic Wallah
Norman Capener

The Anaesthetist
Drs R&M Fortescue Ffoulkes

The Brain Surgeon
Alan Gairdner

Another Physicia
Clifford Fuller

Dr. Charles Wroth

Cartoon Portraits of the staff in 1940 from
'Royal Devon Rudery', the Residents'
play at Christmas, in aid of war weapons.

The Pathologist
Austin Robb

Norman Lock

The Head Man
Mr A Candler

The Junior Physician
Charles Seward

Charlie Carroll

The Senior Physician
Frank Roper

Bobby Worthington

lived in the old nurses' home. Nurses went up a spiral staircase to sleep above the wards in a tiny room with little iron beds. Dress material was scarce; they wore plain light blue. China was stored in the basement and only released against sight of broken pieces, so anyone relieving tension by hurling a plate against the fire escape had to pick it up after. Tea and sugar was weighed out in the storeroom before coming up to the wards. The discipline and strict hierarchy resembled that in the armed forces. Matron spoke only to Sister, Sister to Staff Nurse, Staff to trainee. It was not until there was an emergency when gas workers were brought in from a collapsed trench, and there was no staff nurse present, that Sister addressed Beryl direct.

Some medical patients were put in beds in the Eye Infirmary. The two hospitals had signed a formal agreement in June 1940 to be administered by a Joint Committee. For operations in Southernhay these patients had to be brought across Magdalen Street on a trolley covered with a red mackintosh sheet, then taken back. The only mortuary was in Southernhay, so the deceased made a similar journey (but at least only one-way).

One of the nurses had an infected femur, Norman Capener obtained one of the first penicillin doses from St Mary's Hospital to treat her, and had six firemen standing by for direct blood transfusion – another grateful patient. As antibiotics became available to all after the war, the workload at the PEOH changed; there were still congenital deformities as well as deformities arising from poliomyelitis and tuberculosis, but osteomyelitis and infected joints could be treated quickly. The 'miracle drugs' transformed life in all the hospitals. Mr George Cantrell writes:

Nobody who practised medicine before the appearance of antibiotics can forget the miracle they wrought. Some of the killing diseases – septicaemia, pneumonia, syphilis, mastoiditis, lost their terrors overnight, so quickly did the new drugs cure them. Later came streptomycin for tuberculosis. Abscesses, septic fingers, boils and impetigo disappeared from the outpatient clinic, and the spectre of post-operative infection which had inhibited surgery and brought the fear of operation into folklore gradually receded so that more and more surgery was undertaken.

There was little change in the staff for the duration of the war. The young men were away and the old held the fort. At the Eye Infirmary these old hands were George Hawker and Michael Dykes Bower. Francis Rutter was expected back after serving as an ophthalmic surgeon in the RAMC. He went for a quick refresher course first; 25 years later, Hawker told him that he had never forgiven him for not appearing in Exeter on the day he was demobbed, as he himself had in 1919. Expenditure at the RD&E 1941–51 averaged £45,415 pa, the medical staff still working in a voluntary capacity. Funds came in patchily in 1946, from the Devon & Exeter Butchers' Fete, from the students' Rag and theatrical productions, from Alexandra Rose Day. On 11 November 1946 a Chudleigh resident presented 705 threepenny bits saved during the war years.

HRH Princess Elizabeth visited St Loyes and the Orthopaedic Hospital that month. A week before Christmas 1946 Cresswell Ward was closed because of a shortage of nurses. It was the first time in 200 years that a ward had closed from lack of staff. On the whole, the hospital attracted staff who served with extraordinary dedication. When the porter, William Sylvester Payne, retired in 1947 he had been in the job for 53 years, 47 of them as Head

Porter. Reg Snow worked in the laundry from 1926 to 1972 except for three years during the war. Two senior nurses were to retire in 1963: Miss Ella Eastment, said to have 'uncanny clinical judgement' in 38 years at the RD&E, most as Sister of Summerhayes Ward, and Miss Doris Sanders, 40 years at the RD&E, 35 of them as Casualty Sister, with never a day off sick. She had seen the job title change from 'Accident Room' to 'Casualty Department' to 'Accident & Emergency', and the numbers rise from about ten a day in 1928 to about 80 a day.

On 8 January 1948 a red setter limped into the hospital and lay down across the doorway of one of the wards, and was repeatedly chased out, and kept coming back. Finally someone inspected his paws and found a gash, and once this was washed and bandaged he was happy to leave, a dumb symbol of local expectation of care from their local institution.

There was a drive to attract more nurses in 1947–8 when the hospitals were still full of war-wounded. The incentives were not great: about £3 a month, 48 hours a week, no getting married while training, half a day off between ending night-duty and going on days. Coal boilers in the wards to stoke, heavy screens to shift, floors to polish, and sweep again on Sunday afternoon before visiting hour. They also had to sluice all the laundry, butter bread, patch pinpricks in the surgeons' gloves, pack gauze from a big roll, wash heavy rubber mats, push heavy oxygen cylinders. There was no disposable plastic equipment for intravenous infusions (drips). Everything was glass and red rubber and had to be washed and sterilized and used again. No wonder there was a shortage of nurses.

CHAPTER TWO

5 JULY 1948
A BETTER PROVISION?

hat was it like in those post-war years to stand among the bomb-sites – peace at last but everything else in short supply – and plan a brave new world? At a time of continued National Service, designation of National Parks, nationalization of the railways and the coal mines, the debate raged about the best way to reorganize the health services. Was nationalization the answer here too?

Fund-raisers were finding it increasingly difficult to meet the targets. Anyone requiring treatment found it inefficient and humiliating to have to beg a 'chitty' from a vicar or a rate-payer who would vouchsafe that they were deserving and poor. A war widow, working at Walton's department store and distraught about her sister's illness, would have to go up the carpeted stairs to queue in her lunch-hour outside Mr Walton's office, to beg humbly for a Recommend to the Hospital. But the Hospital House Committee fought for the survival of a system built upon 'self-help and Christian kindness, charitable gifts and human sympathy'. Asked about 'the present taint of patronage' the Hon. Secretary replied, 'I have yet to learn that the desire to serve your fellow creature is a taint'. Nevertheless the need for a more evenly spread and fairer service had long been recognized. And Dean Alured Clarke himself had said about the Winchester hospital: 'Whenever a better provision is made for the sick poor by Parliament, this hospital will cease, or become part of that provision'.

Dr George Stewart Smith, consultant pathologist in Exeter from 1949, had written his MA thesis in Manchester in 1941 on the coordination of hospitals which would be made necessary by the increasing cost of diagnosis and treatment. The 1944 coalition government had proposed combining the administration of voluntary and municipal hospitals, but the BMA was violently against control by local government bureaucrats. The NHS Act of 1946 was a compromise. Local authorities would control community health services but the hospitals would be funded by national government and administered by regional and local boards. Each regional HQ was to be based on a university with a school of medicine. For the South West this was Bristol. The Regional Hospital Boards appointed Hospital Management Boards. This side-stepped any local political pressures. National funding was the only solution if the consultants were to receive salaries in return for their cooperation. But even as the Appointed Day – 5 July 1948 – came and went they were still holding out for the privilege of retaining at least one day a week for private practice, and Aneurin Bevan conceded, admitting that he had 'stuffed their mouths with gold' to keep them in the NHS. In any case, he thought that private practice would soon wither away, because even the wealthy would use the free service.

The consultants were reluctantly 'bought'. They valued their local standing in the community. Each is remembered affectionately as a great 'character'. Alan Gairdner wore a black pinstripe suit, a black 'Anthony Eden' hat, and, since his undergraduate days, in peace and war, in the operating theatre and outside it, he had always worn a monocle. On 5 July 1948 the monocle was replaced in the theatre by spectacles – a gesture of disregard, some thought, towards the Minister of Health. He welcomed the NHS in principle but deplored its extravagance and waste.

No other country set up a state-financed service offering free medical care to the entire population. Could it actually be done?

In the 1940s the West of England Eye Infirmary was one of the few hospitals well enough endowed to run at a profit, from income, subscriptions and legacies. The consultants could see that its substantial capital would be lost in the common pool. They pressed for it to be spent before July 1948 on modernization and new equipment, but the governing body could not change the habits of a lifetime. They were used to conserving assets and never spending capital. The chance was missed except that two private rooms were endowed.

The NHS began with the laudable but unrealistic aim of providing for every medical need 'from the cradle to the grave'. There was an optimistic but completely false belief that once the backlog of untreated illness had been dealt with the nation would be almost too healthy to need hospitals. The newly available antibiotics would control such scourges as TB, and there was the vaccine against polio. The Department of Health really thought that fewer doctors would be needed. St James' ('Jimmy's') in Leeds accordingly dropped its intake of medical students from 70 a year to 50, but soon had to jump back to 200, for there would not be a drop in demand, there would be an uncontrollable rising tide as new treatments were devised, raising greater expectations at greater

expense. Sir Cyril Jones wrote in his 1950 report for Aneurin Bevan that there was a 'fundamental incompatibility between central control and local autonomy' arising from the 'separation of the responsibility for raising and for spending money'. Fifty years after the NHS began no solution has been found. There has to be a cash limit, there has to be a budget, but there must be no 'rationing' of services.

In the City Hospital, when costs rose (and there was significant inflation at the time) it was no longer merely a question of raising the local rates. No longer was Matron in financial control in Southernhay, keeping a strict eye on the price of potatoes and appealing for free ones if they ran out, or for gifts of money if expenses got out of hand. Bevan forbade any appeals for money; in particular, uniformed nurses were not to collect on the streets. The new matron, conscious of the new bureaucratic, less self-motivated structure, congratulated the nurses at their December prize-day: 'The Spirit of Service continues, despite filling in forms'.

Admission to hospital was no longer limited to two per subscribing parish, or men covered by insurance – the national treasury providing the finance had no control over the number of patients referred by their GPs. Dr Tony Daly started his career here in 1948 and was happy to be on a salary, but he saw at once that the NHS would have problems. For six or seven years there were no extra resources put into it, no new beds, everything was in short supply, it just created waiting-lists. The in-patient waiting-list jumped from 181 in January 1944 to 1200 in 1948 to over 2600 in 1950. Derek Jefferiss reckoned that the hospital was only kept going on the goodwill of its staff. George Cantrell remembers:

'Demobilisation began in 1946, and for a year or so the young doctors out of the forces were taking rehabilitation courses and getting extra qualifications. By 1948, the Appointed Day for the NHS, many were in post in the hospitals, taking over the consultant posts.

'They were splendid material; with enormous wartime experience of all sorts of medicine and surgery. Experienced beyond their years too in decisiveness of administration and action, they had an urgency to get on with catching up with backlogs and making the hospitals work.

'It wasn't political expediency that inspired them; they worked together in the hospital service which they saw as theirs, and for whose success they were responsible.

'There were several great years before the political administrators of the NHS found their feet and learned to bureaucratise the smooth running of the hospitals. I remember hearing the Accountant of the SW Region (or some such; part of officialdom routine is the constant change of titles), at a committee. He was red in the face with exasperation as he said "I can control the laundry costs. I can control the expenditure of the kitchens and the running expenses. What I CAN'T control is the consultant's demands for equipment." '

'At this time expenses for equipment were beginning to rise rapidly. Complicated electrical gadgets proliferated, tests in the path. lab. were more complicated and needed complex and accurate machinery. Plastics were replacing the old glass and rubber. Sophisticated medicines from manufacturing firms were taking over – expensively – from the old hospital dispensing pharmacist. Wigs and Spencer corsets for backache, I remember, were quite large items. The hospital consultants were simply not expense-minded and nobody might say them nay.

'Matron Hodges listed the medical staff in office at the RD&E when she came in 1949. Mr Candler had just retired as senior surgeon, leaving the well-established trio of Mr Norman Lock, Mr R. Wayland Smith and Mr Alan Gairdner; for obstetrics and gynaecology Mr P.M.G. Russell and Mr Derek 'Jeff' Jefferiss. Mr Philip Scott had been appointed Ears Nose and Throat (ENT) surgeon. Mr Kenneth Caldwell, a Registrar since 1947, would replace Mr Lock as a general surgeon in 1950. The physicians were the long-installed Drs Seward and Fuller, and new boys Dr John Rowell Simpson and Dr Anthony Daly. (Dr Simpson had taken up duties in June 1947 as honorary dermatologist to RD&E and Torbay Hospitals. This was the first official dermatological appointment south-west of Bristol. Like all the consultants, he was kept very busy – ward rounds and OP clinics all day, then outlying clinics and home visits in the early mornings, evenings or weekends). The radiologists were Dr Wroth and Dr Hadden. Pathologist Dr Stewart Smith. Orthopaedic surgeons based at PEOH but with some beds in RD&E were Mr F.C. Durbin and (from 1952) Mr Cyril Jeffery, 'Jeffery Bones'. '

The NHS had taken over the running of the Princess Elizabeth Orthopaedic Hospital (PEOH) from the Devonian Orthopaedic Association, but the latter continued to hold some of the ground lease, own some of the buildings, organize the welfare side, teaching for child patients, and the workshops where splints and other surgical appliances were made to measure in a smithy from half-inch steel rods. The apprentices scrumped apples and plums from the orchards over the road where the Nuffield Hospital would later stand. 20 beds had been added in 1944 for wartime needs. Barbara Hepworth had made a series of drawings of Norman Capener at work in the operating theatre there, inspired by the atmosphere of concentration and teamwork. She had met him when her triplet daughter was admitted with osteomyelitis. A strong friendship developed and they were to work at sculpture side by side in her studio in St Ives.

Miss Hodges represented the nursing personnel at meetings of the Exeter and Mid Devon Hospital Management Committee in their office at 26 Queen Street. She had been appointed as matron of RD&E, and as 'principal matron' of the Exeter and Mid-Devon Group of Hospitals, having overall responsibility for RD&E, WEEI, City, Mowbray House, and Redhills Hospital. (PEOH had a separate matron, Miss Knapp, who had been appointed in 1929 and was to reign there for forty years.) The WEEI and Mowbray already had matrons in office. City had a resident Master and Matron, positions surviving from when it was a Poor Law and then a Public Assistance Institution – Mr and Mrs Wood, who retired in 1950. Miss Hodges arranged for basic general training to take place at RD&E, and assistant nurses to train at City. By the December 1950 prize-giving she was able to report

Matron Hodges 1949-53.

Child patients in the Princess Elizabeth Orthopaedic Hospital.

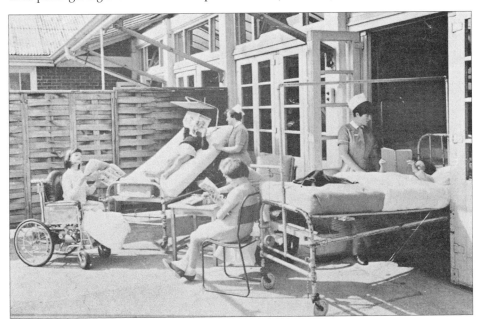

such innovations as the training of male nurses and mental nurses and the part-time employment of married trained nurses. Newcourt House had been bought in the summer of 1945 to use as a Preliminary Training School but six years passed before it was opened by the Countess of Eldon, who pointed out that nurses would be in demand if World War Three broke out. It was the time of the Cold War. There were contingency plans to evacuate the city's hospitals to rural areas.

Most people's memories of the late 1940s include queues – queues in the shops, queues for ration books – and it was no different in the RD&E. Corridors and Out-patients Department were packed, staff were squeezed into tiny offices and it was difficult to function at all. The porter had his little room to the right of the main entrance, with the telephone switchboard behind. Hospital Secretary John Sullivan and other staff had offices to the left. Matron's office and sitting-room were on the ground floor opposite the Resident Doctors' Dining-room and Pantry. Matron's bedroom was on the first-floor next to the operating theatre and over the main entrance through which casualties were admitted during the night. The resident doctors slept on the same corridor. The Nurses' Dining-room was in the basement and very crowded. Matron Hodges was surprised on her first morning to find a long row of nurses outside her office at 8 am wanting 'Late Passes' to stay out until 11 pm. She soon delegated the job of issuing passes to Assistant Matron.

Just before visiting hours, the main entrance and central corridors were blocked with waiting friends and relations. Each patient had two tickets to give out. The situation was improved in August 1950 when the tickets were colour-coded – dark green, light green, yellow, white, blue – and visitors came in via Out-patients and followed arrows to different groups of wards, helped by WRVS and Red Cross volunteers.

Ruth Kelly remembered the pathology laboratory in 1947, on the ground floor of what is now Cecil Boyle House. Their original accommodation had been built in 1934, blitzed in 1942, and now spilled over into two recently erected huts at the back. The technical staff almost had to sit on each other's knees it was so cramped. As a junior, Ruth had to wash up, feed the animals, collect scraps for them, and take blood on the wards.

The pathologist Austin Robb died during the first week of July 1948 just as the NHS got going. His assistant Peter Warren held the fort, even when he contracted viral hepatitis from a syringe and had to work from a side-ward for a month, with a bedside microscope for histology diagnoses. A locum then came from Bristol, and then in May George Stewart Smith, the RD&E's first NHS appointment. The 'path lab' served the whole area including GPs. It was already crowded and inadequate in 1948. From 1949 to 1959 its work expanded fourfold while its staff increased only by one third. George Stewart Smith was in no way opposed to private practice but at the same time was 100% in favour of the NHS and free pathology services for all. He provided these to the highest standards with amazing industry from extremely constricted accommodation – all the while with wit and good humour which was occasionally ghoulish but never irreverent or coarse.

He was elected to the Presidency of the Association of Clinical Pathology, a foundation Fellowship of the Royal College of Pathology; he sat on the South West Regional Health Board (SWRHB), was involved with the Postgraduate Medical Institute and the Northcott Medical Fund, and after retiring in 1969 he chaired the Exeter & Mid Devon Hospital Management Committee. He was awarded the OBE in 1974.

CHAPTER THREE

THE FIFTIES
A QUART IN A PINT POT

Every department was longing for more space. Sister Elsie Treneman, SRN i/c of 'Massage & Electrical Department' moved in 1948 to the Bungalow Ward, where the department was renamed Physiotherapy. When she retired in 1951 there were 5–7 staff. They increased to 8 when Miss Branscombe took over in 1952 but were still only 8 in 1984.

The dark basement contained not only X-ray diagnosis but also radiotherapy, electrocardiogram (ECG), staff canteen, sewing-room, the almoner and, after 1950, an electroencephalogram (EEG) department started by Drs H. Scott Forbes and N.S. Alcock. The latter had been appointed as a neurologist in 1948 to cover the whole SW peninsula.

Matron Hodges resigned to get married in 1950. The new matron, Miss Jean Leiper, could see that a new hospital was not going to materialize in her lifetime. With the help of the Group Engineer, Jack Davis, the ancient building was reorganized to make things easier for patients and staff.

The new Nurses' Home from the 1930s was completely refurbished. Mr Wayland Smith donated a very nice pianola. The Old Home was converted to senior staff quarters. The Theatre Sister who had slept on the Theatre corridor was pleased to be moved, not having had a night's sleep for years. A gen-

Apart from the style of motorcar, this photograph of the front of the hospital in Southernhay can be dated to before August 1960, when a lorry struck a support of the iron-framed glass canopy at the entrance.

eral sterile supply was installed in her vacated room. After a battle with the surgeons, the old kitchen (a relic of 1745) was moved from next to the main operating theatre 'in a cloud of dust and soot and general disgruntlement', and converted into a sluice. Until then, the sluice and sterilizing room were one, using the same hatch, and there was considerable infection present in the surgical wards. Fracture clinics had been held adjacent to the X-ray department. Sixty to seventy patients were seen per clinic. Nobody could move for wheelchairs and plastered legs. Manipulations under anaesthetic and all plaster work was done in the 'shed' at the end of the physiotherapy department. Matron's old quarters were now altered to provide a fracture clinic on the ground floor with easy access from the street. F.C. Durbin had been appointed to PEOH in 1946 and to succeed A.L. Candler with undefined responsibilities at the RD&E. In 1951 he took over the unified Fracture and Casualty Department. C.C. Jeffery was appointed to share the fracture commitment. Fractures treated rose from about 1,000 pa to about 4,500 pa by 1974. A rise in admissions was caused by the number of elderly females fracturing the neck of the femur, and young males in motorbike accidents. Additional beds were used in WEEI and in Victory (ENT) ward, and in Summerhayes (Gynaecology) ward. Out-patient attendance increased proportionately with long queues extending out into the street.

Bleepers were not yet in use, but the switchboard operator could flash various combinations of four coloured lights placed at various points, e.g. green and white, and the appropriate consultant would go to the telephone.

The matron at the WEEI retired and it became an integral part of the RD&E. The main difficulty was the transport of food across the increasingly busy Magdalen Street. Matron Leiper regarded the present traffic lights as her most lasting monument.

In 1948 Mrs E.M. Fordham had joined the almoners' department. Their rooms, now on the first-floor corridor, were cramped but enjoyed a view of the ancient city wall, trees and the cathedral roof. In the outer office the Transport Clerk, Miss Betty Springate, dealt through a hatch with the elderly volunteer drivers and young ambulance men, who queued in the cold and draughty corridor. This office also housed the files, coat hangers and just one chair but there was no room for a second worker. Mrs Fordham and the other almoner, Marjorie Ellis, both had to work in the inner office, which presented problems of confidentiality. To reach their desks they had to pass a remarkably hot and efficient gas fire, watching their longish skirts and overalls. There was no room for the secretary, Miss E.B. Andrew, who was put in the hospital secretary's department. To summon her they knocked on the wall. The almoners helped patients (both in- and out-) with problems related to their illness. They also helped keep acute beds available by arranging transfers to the care of relatives, to convalescent homes or local hospitals. Many of Devon's small hospitals had no almoner service. So from 1951 almoners visited when requested. They also had to deal with problems of admission to hospital.

There were children, animals and birds to be placed elsewhere, old relatives to be settled, and once I had to arrange for a herd of cows to be milked so that the farmer could be kept in after a serious accident.

For the Special Clinic the doctor would ask them to trace contacts –

Go to such-and-such pub look for this woman who generally wears a fur hat, red cardigan and short ginger hair ... So I would go to the

[36]

hostelry, glass in hand, and watch and wait ...

After some years the almoners moved to larger but less gracious offices opposite the paint shop, with room for three almoners and two clerks. The Transport Clerk moved to the Physiotherapy hut.

The mail in the mornings revealed that 'almoner' was not a word known to all. Letters were addressed to the Arms Office, the Alimony Department, the Ottoman, the Falconer etc. But I was sorry when the name was changed to Medical Social Worker.

Mrs Fordham concluded:

The department has always been lucky in its clerks, and there were very few staff changes over the years ... I can never forget the courage and spirit of the sick people of Devon and their love of the hospital which we represented.

X-rays were still being used for both diagnosis and therapy, there being no gamma-ray machines yet. The senior radiologist had stressed in 1944 that radio-diagnosis and radio therapy should be separate departments. Dr Peter Watts was appointed in 1946 and ran the X-ray department almost single-handed. He would dismantle and rebuild the machines until he knew them as intimately as the engine of his 1934 Derby Bentley and if one went wrong he often had it in pieces and put right before the service man arrived. When the image intensifier – one of the first in the UK – (see below) arrived, the first thing he did was take it apart to see how it worked. All X-ray diagnostic procedures for the whole hospital for the next thirty years were provided in the limited basement area, increasingly packed with equipment. The original two ancient machines which sometimes required exposures of up to six minutes were soon supplemented with one modern one. In 1950 film drying and in 1963 automatic film-processing were introduced, and in 1964 image-intensifying; in 1967 overhead suspension, andriography and ultrasound. Volume, variety and turnover of work increased steadily although confined in a department whose physical layout remained unchanged. Dr Peter Watts retired in 1980 just before the arrival of the scanner which he had been fighting to get for six years.

While Dr Peter Watts ran the diagnostic X-ray Department, Dr Wroth's therapeutic X-ray work was helped by the appointment of Dr Ronald Hadden in 1947. 'Ron the Rebel', at 30, was the youngest consultant in the south-west. Like many of his colleagues, he was soon doing the work of three doctors, clinics in the RD&E, weekly clinics in Torbay and every three weeks in the North Devon Infirmary in Barnstaple. He was always rushing from here to there and looking after his private patients as well. Having trained in both diagnosis and therapy he could read his own X-rays; they were sent to Dr Peter Watts but he had usually already established where the trouble was. As he pointed out, he needed to be a specialist in everything, because tumours occur everywhere. He built up 'joint clinics' with, for example, visiting plastic surgeons from Bristol, and a joint ENT clinic with Mr Bradbeer, for treating, say, cancer of the tongue with radium needles. He pioneered work on non-malignant disease of the thyroid glands with iodine therapy. He used X-rays to clear eczema and to loosen ligaments in spondylitis so that patients could straighten up. This would not be allowed now. He took a pride in accurate 'miniaturist' work on, say, a growth on an eyelid. He participated in trials for treatment of cancer of the larynx and of breast cancer. In the latter, he pioneered in the 1950s, with Mr H.

Elizabeth Ward under construction in 1950. Quaker Meeting House, the WEEI and Wynards on the left; Victoria Wing centre back; stores hut roof below it; the covered way of the physiotherapy department.

Dendy Moore, removal of just the lump, not the whole breast – a procedure recently 'rediscovered'.

All the time there was a lack of equipment, a great shortage of beds, and at first no real training facilities. Dr Hadden felt that he was 'making bricks out of straw'. He began pressing for adequate accommodation at the RD&E. 339 new referrals in 1945 had risen to 1788 in 1948 and only five beds were available. Everybody in Southernhay really wanted a large new hospital but meanwhile he campaigned and raised enough money from the public to build a radiotherapy wing. He designed it himself. It took over the gardens of Matron's House and of the Nurses' Home. The radium was stored in a borehole 80 ft deep, to be safe from bombs. The treatment room had a barrel-vaulted roof of insulated reinforced concrete.

Upstairs there were two 6-bed and one 4-bed wards named after Alderman Vincent Thompson (mainstay of the Cancer Fund), Miss A. Stopford-Smyth (retired as matron 1949) and Dr Charles Wroth. Hadden concerned himself with all aspects of the design, down to the smallest details. For taking temperatures, there should not be one thermometer taken right round the ward, but a personal one at the head of each bed. The beds should have curtain screens. St Bridget Nurseries of Exeter laid out a garden of flowering shrubs behind the building, to raise the spirits of patients arriving or looking out of the windows. The building was ready by February 1952. The staff moved the equipment during a week-end. The new wing was called after the new queen, and the first patient also happened to be called Elizabeth.

Dr Hadden arranged for radiotherapy patients from Barnstaple to have bed-and-breakfast accommodation in Newcourt House Monday to Friday during treatment. This saved them the debilitating daily journey, and also saved on hospital car expenses. As for the in-patients, there was a problem arising from tacking the ward on. Patients had to be taken to the main building for anaesthetics, across the tennis courts to the underground corridor and up in a lift to the theatre. If they collapsed on the way back to the ward there was no 'safety net', no immediate post-operative care there. Dr Hadden kept a close eye on patients, seeing them three times a week during treatment, and regularly afterwards.

Dr B. Chudecki joined the Radiotherapy Department in 1955, after an adventurous war in the Polish army and appointments in Liverpool and Charing Cross hospitals. He was appointed to consultant grade in 1963 and retired in 1974. He remembered:

In 1955 the Physics Department was served by Mr R.F. Walker on two visits from Plymouth per week. In 1957 he moved full-time to Exeter. In 1961 the first cobalt unit was installed (G.V. Northcott provided £20,000 for this); in 1963 isotopes were first used in diagnosis and treatment, and in 1966 more effective treatment of deep-seated tumours, through increased penetration with reduced skin reaction was made possible by the second cobalt unit (Devon & Exeter Cancer Fund provided £12,000 for this, which had to be lowered into place through a skylight.)

Mr Jack Griffith the thoracic specialist was appointed to Devon and Cornwall in 1950 but not allotted any beds in Plymouth or Exeter. There was urgent need for surgery for pulmonary TB so he used the sanatorium at Hawkmoor and ran a surgical unit there single-handed for many years. TB patients were kept in open-air chalets. In winter they enjoyed the cold crisp air with snow lying on their blankets.

From 1951 the NHS rented a dozen beds at Poltimore House, a stately mansion standing in parkland five miles from Exeter. Home of the Bampfylde family from 1306 to 1921, this was where Sir Thomas Fairfax negotiated the Treaty for the Surrender of Exeter, bringing an end to the Civil War. It was a girls school from 1923 until 1934, Dover College was evacuated there from 1940 until 1945. Drs R. and M. Fortescue Ffoulkes then ran it as a private nursing-home. He had been anaesthetist at the Eye Infirmary from 1925. His wife was also an anaesthetist and one of the first women doctors in Exeter.

From 1951 until 1962 about 5,000 NHS patients enjoyed the peaceful surroundings, the excellent operating theatre in a converted Tudor kitchen, and the relaxed and happy atmosphere. They had to be carried up and down the sweeping staircase in a sort of hammock, but found it worth it to reach beds arranged around the edge of a ballroom. There was also a Queen Anne room with a plaster ceiling showing the queen with four children round her. The Ministry of Health then took over Poltimore completely (despite warnings of death-watch beetle) but between 1974 and 1987 it reverted to being a private nursing-home.

CHAPTER FOUR

CITY HOSPITAL HELPS OUT

City Hospital was a mixed asset. On the negative side, some of its buildings were unusable, survivals from its days as a Workhouse. Blocks put up in the 1930s for the Municipal Infirmary had suffered damage in the 1942 Blitz. The site is an inconvenient half mile away from Southernhay, and similarly distant from Wonford.

On the plus side, City qualified for war-damage funding for rebuilding, and there was ample space for extra blocks. When the Government imposed a general moratorium on capital spending in 1951 it made sense to upgrade City in order to relieve the pressure on Southernhay, where the operating theatres were in use night and day for most of each week. Drs Alcock, J. Rowell Simpson and Daly were happy to have

Poor Law buildings at City which the Ministry of Health agreed should be replaced in 1939 by a maternity home and nurses' quarters.

the use of a 30-bed ward at City for neurology, dermatology and medical cases, although at first the Junior Medical Staff at City had no accommodation or catering. As numbers increased conditions became cramped here too, but Dr Daly remembers that the atmosphere was always good. Patients found it quieter and more relaxed than Southernhay. 'The facilities were poor but the treatment was better.' There were no pathology or X-ray facilities on site. As Mr Dendy Moore observed, a surgeon without radiological help is like a workman without a thumb. Any patient needing an X-ray was taken to a private surgery in Baring Crescent, until City gained its own X-ray Department in 1955.

Mr Dendy Moore was a meticulous surgeon who achieved excellent results but his perfectionism was not always easy to live with. The theatre staff eventually learnt to disregard his shouting and impatience, as they came to respect

his achievements. Rosemary Longman née Paget recalls:

I was a staff nurse in the operating theatre from October 54 to November 55 only but I remember the appointment of Mr Dendy Moore very plainly. It was probably the contrast from the gentle sessions of minor surgical procedures with Mr Wayland Smith and Mr Lock accompanied by the anaesthetists Dr Walter and Dr Powell. There were also very peaceful bronchoscopy sessions with Mr Griffith, and dental clearances with Mr Selley and Dr Laird. ... Then this brash Australian came to shatter our peacefulness and blast our ears with his language ... I don't think any of us were really prepared for the type of surgery that Mr Dendy Moore embarked upon ... He would demand items such as tampax and egg whisks in the middle of an operation without explaining that the tampax made an excellent plug for the oesophagus and the egg whisk he wanted was the flat scoop type with which to gently retract the lungs ... I told him if he didn't stop shouting and swearing at everyone he would not have any staff left. He told me we were supposed to shout back ... I think what kept us all going was the quiet calm of Dr Powell sitting at the patient's head reading his bible.

Difficulty in obtaining financial support from the Regional Hospital Board for Mr Dendy Moore's project to improve the ventilation in theatre led to a meeting there with the Regional Senior Administrative Medical Officer, James Westwater, before which the surgeon had planted under the table a smoke-bomb manufactured in the works department, ignited soon after the meeting began, filling the theatre with smoke and obliging complete and hasty evacuation in spite of intensive operation of the existing ventilation system. The point was made, new equipment was soon installed.

The other wards at City were still occupied by the long-stay chronic sick, cared for by dedicated orderlies. Only 15% of the staff were trained nurses. In 1953 Clifford Fuller went in a deputation led by Exeter's MP Rolf Dudley-Williams to the Ministry of Health to ask for another 100 general beds for Exeter, in addition to the 40 maternity beds promised, but to little effect. When Miss Helen Graveney took up the post of Matron at City in 1959 the wards were still full of confused, incontinent elderly (mostly women) in cot beds. The noise they made was considerable. Consultant Physician Dr Jack Simpson campaigned vigorously for improvements. By 1953 all he had achieved was cork floors and cubicle curtains.

The new 41-bed maternity unit at City

The Workhouse cell for destitute vagrants. Before leaving they had to do a day's work in the garden or laundry or break stones into pieces small enough to pass through a 2-inch grille. The cells were in use until 1930 and were not demolished until the late 1950s.

came into use in April 1959. It cost £140,000 and had the most modern premature baby unit in the UK. It was opened with a silver key on 13 October 1959 by the Rt Hon. Lady Roborough, blessed by Bishop Wilfrid Westall, and celebrated with a luncheon for 42 in the Southernhay Board Room.

In 1954 Dr Frederick (Freddie) Brimblecombe had joined the staff at Exeter. He was the first of two consultant paediatricians appointed west of Bristol and has been described as 'an ebullient teddy-bear of a man'.

Dr Brimblecombe and Sister Jean Boxall developed the neonatal unit here to such a high standard that patients came from Europe and even further afield. In 1982 Exeter University was to award Miss Boxall an Honorary MA, a unique honour for a nurse.

The Special Care Baby Unit expanded rapidly, managing prematurity, congenital defects of heart and spine, and achieving a fall in neonatal morbidity. Well-wishers knitted tiny bonnets, mittens and bootees.

Brimblecombe's work on infection-control enabled the abolition of mask and gown, so that parents could participate fully in the care of their infants. He was also proud to have established Honeylands Children's Centre as part of the RD&E, providing a comprehensive service for parents bringing up a child with severe disabilities. His obituary in the Times (5 January 1993) celebrated the fact that:

all his life he busily set up systems and established institutions while few fully realised what he was doing. His writings tended to concentrate on the social aspects of paediatrics, and he was a pioneer of this aspect of child health.

He wrote about the unmet needs of children with handicaps and their families, the needs of young adults with disabilities, and he helped train teachers in school counselling.

Clifford Fuller continued to campaign for more beds. Exeter still needed another 100 beds, as it had six years before. He and Norman Capener led another deputation to the Ministry of Health. Dr Jack Simpson pointed out that City had fewer beds for the elderly sick in 1959 (121) than it had in 1939 (132). But 'I do not want more beds, I want better beds.' He wanted the mentally disturbed elderly to be accommodated separately, rehabilitation provided where appropriate, and adequate physiotherapy and chiropody services. £670,000 was allocated, but once again any geriatric beds were squeezed out by cost limits. The only new beds which resulted were for gynaecology and the rebuilt children's ward. The rest was used up by the cost of engineering and heating installations.

More redevelopment at City was announced in 1963, then 1966 and eventually some took place in 1967–70. The site was cleared of all existing buildings except the new maternity unit and four of the older wards. A 4-storey block would have 130 beds in four wards (gynaecology, paediatrics, medical and surgical). There would also be an operating theatre block, a pharmacy block, central sluice block, mortuary and workshop, boiler house, offices for administration and physiotherapy and occupational therapy and an extension to the X-ray department.

Dr Jack Simpson remembers the architect coming, a heavy smoker, waving at the surroundings – 'Do keep these lovely green grounds, people don't like to look out at grey areas of carparking.' That is why there has never been an adequate carpark at City. Vine Cottage on the corner of Gladstone Road was demolished and the hospital's main entrance was moved from Heavitree Road. Professor Caldwell from the Botany department at the University came to advise Estates Officer Geoff Hingston on which trees to

Student nurses February 1969.

keep. 'We'll walk over there. Where's your axe?' He had a piece of chalk in his pocket and marked the trees for felling. Next day Pat Russell rang; the contractors were taking down the ones not marked, three tall fir trees had gone already and they were pulling out the roots with a tractor...

At this time there were changes in the structure of nurses' training. The 'Block' system began. Nurses had to have an eight-week introductory course then four- or six-week blocks of classroom teaching to a total of 28 weeks over two years. In 1969 there was a ruling that hospitals with less than 200 beds could not be training schools. Exeter therefore brought together the student nurses of City and Southernhay into a new 'Group Training School for the Register and Roll of Nurses'.

Dr Jack Simpson was still campaigning for improved geriatric services. Dr Bill Wright was appointed as the first full-time geriatric consultant. Matron Graveney remembered the changes which resulted.

Now patients were investigated and treated. They had to get up, dress and move about (much against the will of some of them). Activity was the treat-ment, involving the Physiotherapist and the Occupational Therapist. Day rooms were found from somewhere. The Unit became an investigation and short-term treatment unit, and later offered day-care. Dr Simpson reports:

Finally, after eight years of squawk-ing, we achieved a lift. Until then all patients in Heale and Seaward wards had to be carried up two flights of stone stairs. I suppose it deterred some from escaping. The improvements were catalysed by two events. The first was a medical-ly inspired press campaign 'Sans teeth, sans eyes, sans everything'. The second was the fire.

There was a tragic fire in Seaward Ward at 1 am on 13 February 1970 when a mentally confused elderly patient lit a fire under his bed. Firemen wearing breathing apparatus evacuated all the occupants of the ward but five later died from the effects of smoke. The mattress-es were foam-filled and produced toxic black fumes. Patients from the other wards were taken to Southernhay in a double-decker bus, some from post-operative intensive care. Sister Nona Kerslake and the student nurses she was training went to scrub the sticky black soot off the beds and lockers as a practical expression of the fact that City and Southernhay were partners now in the Group Training School.

In May 1972 funding was announced at last for a 100-bed geriatric block, to be ready by 1976. The wards would be called after eminent former Exonians rather than 'Block A' or 'Block B' as in Infirmary days. The names chosen included Seaward (first Governor of the City Hospital) and Pereira Gray (first doctor). The maternity wards are now called after famous local Elizabethans (Bodley, Hilliard, Hooker) and the central block commemorates donors of Exeter almshouses (Atwill, Dinham, Hurst and Wynard).

The wards for care of the elderly have 4-bed bays and singles; men and women have separate day rooms. In March 1979 a therapeutic garden was laid out below Polsloe Road, with raised flower-beds and wheelchair-friendly paths. This is little used now because the hospital does more acute work and less rehabilitation. In the podiatric corridor the walls have been transformed by a street-scene mural. The artist was Rachel Lewis.

In the next few years all these specialities are due to move to Wonford too starting with care of the elderly in April 1998. Only the remaining stretches of the elaborate eight-foot-high brick boundary walls of the Workhouse built here just 300 years ago will mark the place where so many of us first got to know our babies, or said fond last farewells to elderly relatives.

CHAPTER FIVE

MEANWHILE, BACK AT THE RD&E

Dr Clifford Fuller OBE,
Mayor 1956–7.

The doctors and surgeons of the hospital were so much part of Exeter's social fabric that it seemed natural to honour one or two particularly worthy ones with the mayoralty. Until 1974 the mayor did not have to be an elected councillor. Mr John Haddy James had been mayor in 1828 and Thomas Shapter in 1847. Mr Wayland Smith was chosen in 1952 and Dr Clifford Fuller in 1956. Wayland Smith's term of office was remembered by the fact that he allowed the ancient Trinity Burial Ground, regarded as an elegant feature of Southernhay West, to be replaced by public toilets. They were convenient for visitors to the hospital but were nicknamed Wayland's Folly.

The Duchess of Gloucester presented awards at the Nurses' Annual Prize-giving in December 1956, and toured the wards, and took tea in a marquee on the tennis court. Pigs had not been kept in the back yard here for 150 years, but it was still a time of austerity. Mr Gairdner, known as 'Pop', drove a battered black Standard car towing a trailer holding four dustbins overflowing with swill from the wards for 'Pop's pigs'. There were no parking problems then. Only the doctors had cars. Nurses, sisters and others either walked to work or cycled. The doctors parked next to Outpatients. Gairdner specialised in orthopaedics, after experience of cerebral surgery in the US and of chest wounds during his war service. After the war, fractures were taken over by

Matron Jean Leiper and staff 1957.

orthopaedic specialists, cerebral cases were sent to Bristol and Mr Griffith set up his thoracic unit. Gairdner turned to neonatal and genito-urinal fields until he retired in 1965.

A new development in 1956 was that relatives of seriously ill patients were able to stay overnight at the hospital. One single and one double bedroom were built with funds donated by the Trustees of the Devon Queen Victoria and King Edward Commemoration Funds.

Mrs Ethel Cann trained as a student nurse in Southernhay in the 1950s:

We all spent our first months literally in the sluice, washing all the linen, counting the sheets, and cleaning, but we were all so proud of wearing the traditional cap and aprons (well ironed at 10 o'clock every morning after doing the cleaning).

Staff nurses wore bows when qualified. Only sisters wore the goffered cap, which involved complicated manoeuvres with starch and a toothbrush and had to be gathered with a thread after each weekly laundering. It had strings which tied in a bow under the chin. Those who found it uncomfortable would flip the string over the top at night. When Ruth Furze became matron she thought the existing staff had rather a 'farmer's daughter' image. She had trained at St Thomas's, and encouraged nurses from there to come to Exeter. All the sisters wore dresses of navy blue material with tiny white spots, as worn at St Thomas's. Matron had a ruler fourteen inches long. All uniform dresses had to be fourteen inches from the floor, whether the nurse was short or tall. The nurses' capes were held by two long strips inside which crossed at the front and buttoned at the back. For harvest festival they would process to the cathedral in indoor uniform, with capes reversed to show the red lining. The Bishop let them use the short cut through his garden from the main entrance of the hospital. Matron would be standing with her watch checking the time as the last nurse ran up pulling on a second white glove.

The lay-out of the wards was still unchanged from the epoch-making day when the head of each bed was set against the wall. This was called a Nightingale ward and was the arrange-

Ruth Furze, Matron 1958–70, painted by Beryl Newman (1969).

ment favoured at St Thomas's. A series of postcards issued before the First World War shows the wards decorated elaborately for Christmas but otherwise very much the same as they still were in the 1950s – long rows of beds to left and right. The wards were still heated by coal fires. The only improvement was that heavy screens had been replaced by screens on wheels, and then with half-length draw curtains. By April 1958 three of the 38-bed wards in the Victoria Wing had been transformed, using money from donations and legacies. In Summerhayes, Dawson and Dean Clarke, the long row of beds on one side was replaced with 4-bed recesses. An ultramodern convenience for nurses and patients was the installation of tuberail curtain screens. The checked curtains were provided as 'patients' comforts' by the hospital's League of Friends. At first the curtains bunched by the wall when pulled back, stopping conversation between neighbouring beds, but the estate office adjusted the fittings to bend back along the wall. The heating and lighting were also upgraded. Each ward took twelve weeks to renovate. Clifford Fuller bet Geoffrey Hingston two and sixpence that they would not do Dean Clarke Ward, the heart ward on the top floor, in the twelve weeks allowed. They did, and Fuller paid out the half-crown. When Matron Furze came, she was shown plans for modernising Newcourt and Cresswell Wards, but no start-date had been set. One morning Mr Gairdner was on his ward-round in Cresswell and

On Christmas Eve nurses carrying
lanterns sang carols in the wards then
processed to the midnight service
at Holy Trinity Church.

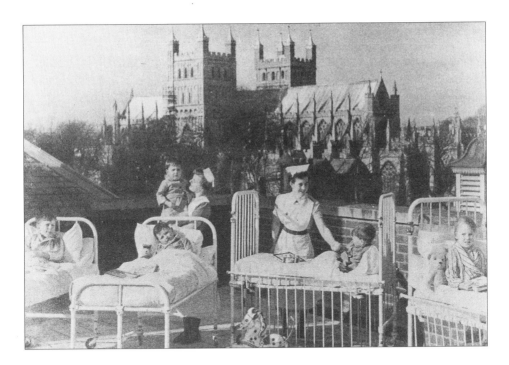

Bowring, the children's ward, uses the rooftop to enjoy the sunshine, the fresh air and the view of the Cathedral.

sent for matron. The charge nurse had just told him that the nurse preparing a dressing trolley in the sterilizing room (which was actually on one of the balconies) had to wear a mackintosh because the rain was coming in on him and on the sterile trolley. Mr Gairdner rang the Regional Hospital Board (RHB) and the Management Committee and the go-ahead for modernisation came through soon after.

City's new maternity unit was not ready at the Estimated Time of Arrival. So many mothers had booked in for it that the 12-bed maternity ward in Southernhay was very busy for its last few weeks in 1959. After that it became a surgical ward then eventually an isolation ward of three beds.

During Dr Brimblecombe's first month in Exeter in 1954, an out-break of gastro-enteritis in Bowring Ward had exposed the urgent need for improved isolation and barrier nursing facilities. The Hospital Management Committee could not find the cash for cubicles. A timely leak to the press from the RHB in Bristol brought publicity, the finance materialized and the epidemic did not recur.

Dr Brimblecombe asked his house physician to sleep in the attic and vacate the bedroom next to the maternity ward so that it could be used to treat premature babies. In 1959 when the Premature Baby Unit moved to City, the vacated two-bed ward became a 'Head Injury & Respiratory Failure Unit'. Dr J. Powell the senior anaesthetist had been to Holland to help with the polio epidemic, using iron lungs. On his return he was determined to start such a unit in Exeter realising that head injuries often succumb not to their injury but from being unconscious, leading to breathing problems. This became one of the first Intensive Care Units in the west country.

Miss D. E. Looseley, Sister in charge of the Unit, described it for the 1964 issue of the Nurses' League Magazine:

All the cubicles and partitions that were present for the premature babies have now disappeared. Along the right hand wall as you enter, cupboards have been installed, glass fronted cupboards at eye level fixed to the wall, and from the floor are more cupboards and drawers covered with a formica working surface. The room contains two tipping type beds with detachable head pieces, two suction machines, two square trolleys, two respirators and usual ward equipment.

Many conditions may affect normal breathing mechanism; for example, Barbiturate overdose, post-anaesthetic respiratory failure, Bronchitis, Emphysema, Asthma, Encephalitis, Chest injuries, all of which have been treated in this unit. A constant vigilance is required for all these patients, conscious or unconscious, day and night. Many of these patients have been given continuous artificial respiration by means of the mechanical respirators:

Together with a team of doctors, which includes a consultant anaesthetist and a consultant surgeon and/or physician, it is the nursing staff who carry out the major part of the treatment of these patients ... The physiotherapists work with the team of nurses ... During the short time that this unit has been in use we have been encouraged by the recovery that some of these patients have made.

On 22 October 1959 the Express & Echo printed a photo of rows of people waiting in Out-patients, and some comparative figures.

	1939	1949	1959
No. of beds	280	300	322
Admissions	4,750	6,287	7,663
Operations	3,128	4,939	10,402
OP attendances	56,081	64,336	112,064

CHAPTER SIX

THE SIXTIES
'TOMORROW TO PASTURES NEW'

The staff at Southernhay continued to long for a move to spacious modern premises. From the 1940s Exeter had been hoping for a new hospital on a larger site. In 1944 the Honorary Staff of the RD&E under the Chairmanship of Senior Surgeon A.L. Candler had produced a report. They foresaw the need for expansion, more than there was room for at Southernhay, and they were the first to propose 'a large new hospital of 700 beds, south of the city near Countess Wear'. In 1949 the Exeter & Mid-Devon Hospital Management Committee, meeting in its offices at 26 Queen Street, had proposed that a new general hospital be built on the Wonford Hospital estate. The suggestion was hotly resented by the Devon Mental Hospital Management Committee as it threatened the demolition of Wonford House. But in February 1950 the RHB in Bristol approved the idea and decided to press the Minister of Health for immediate agreement on this site. In December 1950 Dr Harry Hall-Tompkin (an Exeter GP) was still reporting a shortage of rooms and of staff – a new hospital was the only answer. Dame Georgiana Buller said that after a long life as an agitator she was convinced that nothing was ever done unless one shouted long and hard. But in 1951 the government announced the ban on capital expenditure. Hopes subsided until 1960 when the Minister of Health Derek Walker-Smith was in Exeter and inspected the Wonford site.

It lay on a prehistoric ridgeway, near the ancient village of Wonford, which had been head of the Saxon hundred which stretched as far as Okehampton. A thousand years later the Health Area had the same territory. The Saxon courts were held beneath a landmark tree at Wonford, called the Capital Tree, the Head Tree, heofod treow, Heavitree. Across a Saxon lane lay the PEOH. On the site itself, Wonford House, an Elizabethan-style limestone palace, had been built in 1866–9 to house 120 mentally ill ladies and gentlemen and their staff. Its grounds were now used as playing-fields by Endsleigh School, St Margaret's School and University of Exeter women's teams, the Christchurch cricket field and public allotments. The patients could go for a good long walk without leaving the grounds.

Enoch Powell became Minister of Health in 1961 and soon announced a vast programme of new district general hospitals and a definite start on Wonford in 1964. When 1964 came the start was limited to pathology laboratory and public health laboratory, which would be opened in July 1966. The replacement of the main hospital was put off in 1967 for yet another year. So for the first 25 years of the NHS, Exeter's hospitals functioned on cramped sites, separated from each other by distances which ranged from just across the road (WEEI) to many miles (Poltimore, Hawkmoor, Newcourt). Honeylands was at Whipton, two miles from Southernhay, and Mowbray Maternity Hospital in Heavitree was three quarters of a mile from the related support services at Gladstone Road.

In 1962 the General Nursing Council

Newcourt House, Old Rydon Lane, whose story intertwines with that of the RD&E.

for England & Wales brought in a new syllabus: three years' training, and the introduction must be given in hospital. Newcourt was given up.

From January 1963 Newcourt was used for residential care of the young chronic sick. There were 28 beds on the ground floor, with level access to the beautiful grounds. The venture was regarded as worthwhile and successful for 20 years. When Newcourt was vacated the teacher for the preliminary nursing course used a room in the basement of the Nurses' Home for the introductory eight weeks. They learned practical caring skills involving the use of dummies before being let loose on real patients. They also learned how to sterilize equipment, give out drugs and how to assist medical staff with increasingly complex skills.

Miss Mary Brown, Principal Tutor 1952–71, was very strict. Nobody could leave the class till 5 pm. If the lesson was finished at ten to, she might put on an educational film which lasted til 5.45.

Room was found for more 'temporary' wooden huts behind the RD&E, for the Teaching Department of the Nurses' Training School. The Chairman of the SW Regional Hospital Board cut a tape in July 1962 to declare the huts open, and the Chaplain blessed their future use.

When Mr Keith Vowles joined the staff that year he was one of four 'general' surgeons. The others were Mr Gairdner, Mr Caldwell and Mr Shaldon. Everybody was 'general' except the two gynaecologists. They all ate together in the doctors' dining-room next to the Board Room. It had the atmosphere of a club. Prof. David Mattingly, then a Residential Medical Officer, also remembers how 'matey' it was:

> In the course of a day you would meet everyone. You would accost a colleague over lunch, ask them to look at a patient, go off to the ward together and talk freely about the problem over coffee after.

Keith Vowles also mentions how easy it was to discuss a case. You could go to the pharmacist, go to Matron Furze, 'Is it a good idea to do so-and-so?' Out of hours, the key to the pharmacy was in the porter's lodge. Doctors could take drugs and sign the book.

The consultants were 'matey' to each other, but among the nurses there was still a strict hierarchy.

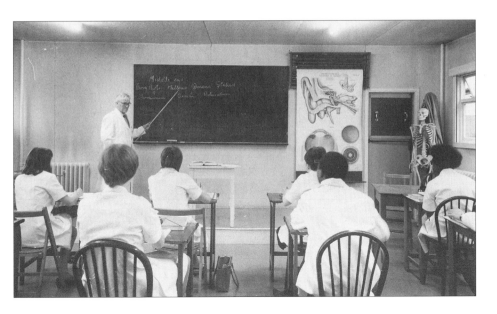

Frank Williams teaching in the School of Radiography, which had its own badge, certificates and prize-giving. Mr Clifford Walker taught physics there. Miss Suzanne James followed Mr Williams as principal teacher.

The rules included not making friends with seniors, standing aside for senior nurses, (even 6 months senior) on the stairs and not chatting to the domestic staff, who each carried a specific title such as 'ward maid' or 'matron's maid.' (Now they are all called housekeepers.)

Monica Hadden also recalls the extremely busy Out-patients Department under Sister Evans, known to everybody as Marj. But when a male nurse came running in one morning and said 'Hallo Marj,' there was a terrible silence. Sister Evans is remembered as an excellent teacher for third-year student nurses working in OP before their finals. 'She stressed that the patient came first.' … All this was not easy in an overcrowded department with medical records people in and out and doctors coming in late and several clinics going on at once.

In 1962 Mrs Forman was appointed to the new post of Infection Control Sister,

only the second in the country, at the instigation of Dr Stewart Smith and Dr Brendan Moore. Dr Moore had run the Public Health Laboratory in Dix's Field from 1945, in Gandy Street from 1959, and was to share the Wonford Pathology Laboratory building from 1966. He was an authority on phage typing of staphylococci and with the arrival in England from Australia in 1955 of the penicillin-resistant 'hospital staph' he was in a unique position to advise on how to combat the spread of infection, especially in surgical wards and among young infants. Sister Forman obtained the best results at City with the cooperation of Mr Dendy Moore. Any surgical infection was immediately transferred to Whipton Isolation Hospital, and the ward would be closed for disinfection and checks made on air, bedding, patients, nurses and medical staff. The practice of squeezing in extra beds was discontinued. Woollen blankets were replaced with cotton, which could be laundered at a higher temperature. Later, disposable sheets came in. Steam sterilizers were removed from the wards and a Central Sterile Supply Department was set up with funding from the Regional Board.

Norman Capener retired from the

PEOH in 1963 after a distinguished career. With the Devonshire Appliance Organization he had devised such gadgets as the Lively Fingers Splint with which the patient could exercise the hand with springs and wires. He had been Vice-president of the Court of Examiners of the Royal College of Surgeons, scientific director and later chair of the Medical Commission on Accident Prevention, and gave expert advice, for example, on the design of seat-belts. After retirement he worked tirelessly to further Exeter's interests.

BBC TV recorded Songs of Praise in the RD&E Chapel in December 1963. Nurses, doctors and some of the patients formed the congregation. Others followed the service from loudspeakers and screens in the wards. The interspersed illustrations of hospital life included the Chaplain knocking at the main entrance when summoned in the night.

Many pioneering schemes sprouted in the cramped seed-bed of Southernhay. One significant venture was the Postgraduate Medical Centre which had long been promoted by Drs Seward, Fuller, Capener, Daly, Stewart Smith, Brimblecombe and colleagues. It finally took off in 1963 in a hut in the grounds, with a small library, classroom, small lab, one or two offices and a toilet. Matron had to give up more of her garden and the croquet lawn. Dr David Mattingly became the first director. He had been in Southernhay before, as Residential Medical Officer in 1955, and remembered that the only medical library then was in the consultants' sitting-room, where there were 16 or 17 donated journals that juniors were allowed to read in the evenings.

The Centre was founded with profits from motor car manufacture. Clifford Fuller had attended a Nuffield Conference in Oxford on postgraduate education. There was funding available from Viscount Nuffield's Provincial Hospital Trust. Exeter was one of the first projects to get off the ground, with a five-year priming grant. The purpose was to provide in-service training and refresher courses for doctors, many of whom came from abroad. GPs wanted short courses, but when further funding was needed in 1968 it would be easier to secure for full-time courses. Dr Mattingly's solution was to start one-term full-time courses. About one thousand students did one term or more, including ex-servicemen, married women returning after starting a family, career changers, but mostly overseas doctors needing an introduction to UK hospitals before taking up posts.

Exeter University provided lectures on non-medical subjects. Dr Stewart Smith pointed out, 'This is the first time that such a centre will have been started in association with a university without a medical school.' After five years it might have had to close down, but Vice-Chancellor Llewellyn took David Mattingly to the chairman of the University Grants Committee. Sure enough, the tone changed at the mention of 'full-time' students. The South West Region was also very supportive. The 10-week courses in medical practice attracted doctors not only from the UK but also from Greece, India, Iraq, Pakistan, Bolivia, Iran, Mexico, Southern Rhodesia. There was a clear need for larger premises. Norman Capener met G.V. Northcott on a train (they were both always going to London for meetings) and persuaded him to donate £100,000 from his Northcott Devon Medical Foundation towards a new building at Wonford. The NHS also put money in, realising that extra training improved patient care. The Centre was officially opened in October 1970 by G.V. Northcott's daughter, Mrs G. Clark, with an inaugural lecture by Prof. Sir J. McMichael, director of the British Postgraduate Medical Foundation. The Centre contained a lecture theatre, library, museum, committee room and common room. Some of the oil paintings were removed from the Southernhay Board Room to hang here to inspire later generations. In 1973 a chair of Postgraduate Medical Studies was created for the Centre's director, Prof. David Mattingly. Dr Brimblecombe was given an honorary Chair of Child Health in 1979 and his research unit became a department of the Postgraduate Medical School. Among other projects, he investigated perinatal deaths in the Exeter area, drew up the first register of congenital malformations and set up the south-west's first genetic counselling service. The numbers of overseas students fell rapidly after the huge rise in their fees in 1979. In 1987 Dr Denis Pereira Gray (later also Professor) succeeded Professor Mattingly as Director. There is some disappointment among those who struggled to establish the Postgraduate Medical Institute (PGMI) that it has not so far led to an undergraduate medical school in Exeter. However it has been able to win a world-wide reputation for training postgraduates with a heavy clinical bias, and for significant research related to the needs of a defined local population.

At first the PGMC did not do anything about general practice. It was mostly concerned with training doctors to take higher degrees, especially those with overseas qualifications. Traditionally general practice had been passed down from father to son with no special training. Things were different now. GPs needed to understand the increasingly complicated technology. The DHSS agreed to fund a Department of General Practice from 1973.

The Hippocratic oath is a reminder of the early training of doctors around 400 BC by the Greek Hippocrates on the island of Cos, under the branches of a large plane tree. A descendant of this tree was planted on the Wonford campus to shelter the postgraduate medical students, but with regard to the north-ern climate and advances in technology the Department of General Practice was also provided with a £29,000 building, opened in April 1976 by Professor Patrick Byrne, President of the Royal College of General Practitioners, and Vice-Chancellor Harry Kay. Dr D.J. Pereira Gray was to be Senior Lecturer here, and run 3-year courses which would eventually produce 10 GPs each year. Many GPs work single-handed and can feel isolated. Here they can meet each other, attend lectures and use a good medical library. The Northcott Devon Medical Foundation continues to fund research at the PGMI e.g. the genetic causes of rheumatoid arthritis; heart block and pace-makers; swallowing in infants and in the elderly (in cooperation with the university's Physics Department. Such cooperation is invaluable. The doctors know what clinical problems there are, and have ideas about solving them, but the university staff have the expertise, the laboratory facilities and the time).

In the 1950s and again in the 1960s Exeter took part in an integrated scheme of training with the Hospital for Sick Children in London. The Great Ormond Street nurses in their pretty little white caps came for general experience. Exeter Training School became nationally known in 1964 when a team of three student nurses won the Marion Agnes Gullan trophy competition in London open to all training schools.

Sometime in 1964 Dr Harry Hall asked Matron Furze what she thought about starting a renal dialysis unit. She was against any more small departments, but before she had replied he had installed a KOLFF 'artificial kidney' in a side-ward, with salts in a drum and tubes taking the blood in and out. This saved patients travelling to Bristol. He then adapted Whipton Isolation Unit for dialysis. The Isolation Hospital at Whipton, once full of patients suffering from diphtheria, scarlet fever and chicken-pox had become redundant since these diseases lost their virulence. The first kidney transplants in Exeter were carried out in 1969. There were 25 operations in the first five years. The number was to pass 400 by the time that such operations stopped in Exeter in 1997.

Hip-joint replacements began at the PEOH in 1965 with six pioneering operations. Two hundred were done before 1970 when numbers accelerated, the PEOH being one of four British centres licensed to do these operations. The Ling-Lee joint was developed here by Robin Ling, Consultant Orthopaedic Surgeon and Honorary Professor of Bioengineering at Exeter University, and engineering scientist Dr Clive Lee. When they heard it reported as a Chinese invention they changed the name to the Exeter Hip. This became the standard across the world. By 1987 the PEOH had done 600 replacements and 100 revisions. The team were continually improving the device and in 1988 launched the Exeter Universal Hip. The components are made by a manufacturer and the finished joints are produced at a rate of 9,000 pa. Replacement knee joints began in 1984 and about 100 were done in 1988.

Exeter is also known around the world for another local invention: the Exeter Coil – a below-the-knee calliper.

Lung cancer had been attributed to cigarette-smoking in 1953, but presentations to retiring staff in the Board Room did not take any notice of this for many years. When the Deputy Head Porter Ivor Caseley retired in 1965 after nearly 18 years in the job, he was given a silver cigarette lighter, cigarette box and cigarettes.

Mr Michael Dykes Bower retired from the WEEI in 1965. He was the last man in Exeter to employ a butler, and almost the last private resident of Southernhay. He came into work once white with fury because for the first time he had not been able to park outside his house. Michael Dawrant joined Mr Cantrell

and Mr Rutter at the WEEI in 1965. The consultants were supported by one dispensing optician and later one sight-testing optician. Dr Dawrant ran three clinics, including one for contact lenses and one for children. After three years of repeated requests the city's school health committee provided a nurse.

The NHS says it is short of money now, but it really was short then. The equipment was Victorian. It took a year to get a washbasin for the contact lens clinic and a year to get £50 for a basic fitting set.

There was no secretarial support. Consultants wrote their own letters in longhand. This made for short letters, such as Mr Roper's shortest ever, 'I will have him in and get it out.'

When Dr Dawrant started a glaucoma clinic in 1965 he had to make the appointments himself. Otherwise there was no appointment system for years. People came at eight, the waiting-room would be full at 8.30, first come first served. Ward round at 8.30, then the doctors would work through to 7 or 8 pm until they had seen everybody, snatching a coffee and sandwich when they could. From 1956–66 the WEEI had been expecting its Out-patients Department to be demolished to make way for the projected Bull Meadow flyover, so there had been no modernising or redecoration. In fact it had not been painted since the 1930s. Minor ops took place in the corridor of Out-patients. Flakes of paint would fall into the patient's eye. George Cantrell remembers the pervading smell of burnt milk. The nurses would be talking to patients and forget they had put it on to heat.

In May 1966 a new boiler was installed in Southernhay to provide the steam for heating, cooking and laundry. There was no interruption to hospital services. Those with Haden tea-kettles may like to know that this giant boiler was installed by Haden & Sons Ltd.

Mrs C.M. Quicke, JP, of the local family famed for their cheeses, retired in 1966, having served on the Management Committee and the House Committee and chaired the Nursing Committee. She is remembered as having been a good friend to the hospital and to the nursing staff for many years.

There was no separate anaesthetics department until a seventh specialist consultant was appointed in 1966 with four juniors. Thirty years later there are now 18 consultant anaesthetists and about the same number of juniors. In 1966 in Southernhay the department was given a secretary and a small office. (When the new hospital was being planned nobody thought to allot offices to the growing department. They thought anaesthetists just needed stools at the end of the operating table. At the last moment they begged for their own building or at least to have a courtyard filled in. There was no money for this, they had to use the patients' branch of the public library. So it was a bonus for the anaesthetists that the 1970s hospital had to be demolished. In the new hospital built in the 1990s they were able to stake a claim for a suite of officers and a lecture-room adjacent to Intensive Care.)

The first building on the new site at Wonford was the combined Pathology (two and a half floors) and Public Health (one and a half floors) Laboratories.

Dr Westwater, Senior Administrative Medical Officer of the SWRHB had said at the sod-cutting in March 1964, 'This is an act of faith and I will see to it that within two years there will be a major hospital on this site.'

The laboratory had a reinforced concrete frame, faced with brick and white rough-board formwork concrete, with windows framed in anodised aluminium. The laboratory fittings were made from natural West African teak. A helicopter landing-pad was outside but hardly used until the Air Ambulance got going. There was a vacuum-tube system which would speed specimens to and fro between pathology and the new hospital, but for another eight years specimens needing immediate examination would have to be rushed from Southernhay by taxi. Access was from Church Lane to what would eventually be a ring-road round the whole site. Parking for 50 cars was provided in a dip for concealment.

The building was opened on 30 June 1966 by the Chief Medical Officer of the Ministry of Health, Sir George Godber. 'The staff might feel that they had moved from log cabins into the White House.'

Dr Tom Hargreaves was appointed as Consultant Chemical Pathologist a month after the opening and developed a superb diagnostic service. He won an international reputation for liver disease research. The new laboratory was able to handle greatly increased numbers of requests:

1958	1963	1968	1973	1978
61,103	104,658	176,970	270,303	425,558

By 1970 the SWRHB would accept that it had been too small from the start and planned an extension for Chemistry, Electron microscopy, Blood transfusion and other services. But in 1973 funds were cut again and only two small huts were added. It was another ten years before an extra storey, the 'Animal House' was put on.

In 1967 Sheila Barnard was interviewed in the Board Room and taken on for a trial period as Reception Liaison Officer. She sat at a table in Out-patients, facing the rows of benches where patients waited for hours. She had to keep track of who was there, who had gone for a blood test or to a clinic, if a nurse or a car driver came asking. She had to jiggle the queues for six or seven clinics, sometimes giving precedence to

The 1968 fire. The royal coat of arms is prominent.

someone with a crying child or a desperate need to get home soon.

On a freezing winter night, 22 February 1968, just after 7 pm the fire alarms went off in Southernhay. A fire in the roof above the kitchen spread into a lift shaft. Flames roared 60 ft high from the roof and destroyed the original cupola. Fortunately there were no wards in the central block any more and no lives were lost. Sixty firemen fought the blaze. 130 patients were carried to safety in their beds, or dragged on mattresses, in an efficient evacuation which took only 14 minutes. The Civil Defence was holding a First Aid class in Barnfield Hall and were quickly summoned, as were the boys of the Spartan Boxing Club in the Trinity Youth Centre, to help the Red Cross and St John's Ambulance. People came from miles, not all to help. Some, knowing the need for a new building, offered to fan the flames. The paintings and furniture from the Board Room were carried to the car park, and

later to the Royal Albert Museum for temporary storage. Sister Slade called the nurses to push the furniture in the Nurses' Home against the walls to make room for patients on the floor. Others were taken by bus or ambulance to hospitals at Franklyn, Poltimore, Whipton and Exminster. Sheila Barnard remembers standing by the bus doors asking the name, ward and destination of each patient so that their notes could be sent after them by police car. The nursing officer brought jugs of tea. 'And who came round at 2.30 am with scrambled eggs and bread and butter? – Matron.' By Saturday 24 February six wards were reoccupied. The Board Room was fitted out as a temporary kitchen after its floor had been reinforced and the panelling boxed in. Meanwhile the electricity and gas offices and Walter Otton's hardware store all opened on the Sunday and their staff came to put in new pipework. The first meals were served from there on the Monday. There were three weeks of wonderful food while the builders and scaffolding men were being fed by four cooks instead of the usual one. The

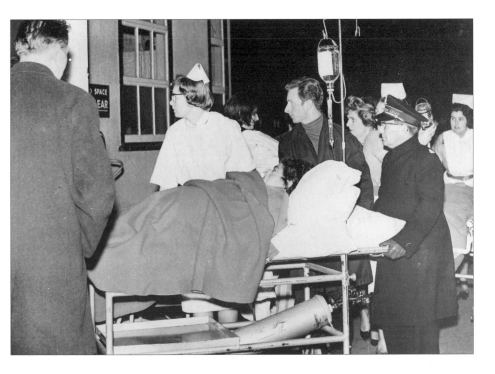

All patients were safely evacuated in 14 minutes.

weather-vane from 1742 survived the fire. The cupola was replaced by a low-maintenance fibre-glass replica, octagonal with steel frame and polyester 'glazing', 16 ft high, 7 ft 6 ins wide.

The Salmon Report swept aside the positions of Matron and Ward Sister in 1968 and brought in 'Nursing Officer Grade VII' and 'Senior Nursing Office Grade VIII' and other grades designated by number. Matron Furze felt the change deeply and personally. Many of the doctors deplored the loss of a figure to whom anyone from student nurse to senior consultant could go for a hearing and a decision on nursing problems.

Ex-Matron Hodges, writing in 1984, said:

Now, the problem is passed up the scale of administration, and by the time a decision, if any, is made, the crisis may well be over, possibly with an unfortunate result.

She also felt that nurses had less dedication, less vocation – there was 'no-one in charge', no matron in loco parentis to represent advice and discipline.

In March 1970 visiting members of the College of Physicians gathered in the Board Room for a lecture. They were greatly surprised when Sir George Baker (who had died in 1809) appeared to enter, and deliver his lecture of 1767 on the 'Devonshire Colic' which arises from the presence of lead in the cider presses. Prof. David Mattingly had conspired with Tony Church, director of the Northcott Theatre, to dress in costume and bring off this illusion.

In the 1970s Prof. David Mattingly and David Knowles found that there was no check on the handing out of medicine on the wards. They devised a form, still in use, with columns to tick that drugs had been given, and when, and (initials) by whom. It was a new idea to have the pharmacist come on ward rounds. Previously there had been large bottles of tablets in each ward, standing there maybe for years. Now the ward pharmacist was to check all the prescriptions once a week. A bottle was to come labelled with the patient's

Nurses in the Dining-room at Southernhay.

name, and to leave when the patient left.

Val Trower was a part-time ward-clerk at Southernhay in the early 1970s. Computers were not yet introduced. Matron had a card-index of the patients. Medication was now carefully controlled. As clerk, Val had to update patients' files with path. lab. results, take samples to the path. hut, carry heavy 24-hour urine jars down the concrete steps. Clerks were not allowed to use the lift unless accompanying a patient. They were told that if they had any time over they were to do the flowers and chat to patients, but there never was any time over.

The PGMC brought computers to Exeter hospitals. One piece of research there funded by the Northcott Devon Medical Foundation was a one-year epidemiological study of disease in the Exeter population, collecting information from GPs. Dr N.G. Pearson was brought from Wales to direct this project. He and Professor John Ashford began using a computer to process the data, and were in the right place when the Exeter Computer Project was suggested.

The Department of Health & Social Security (DHSS) funded experimental computer projects in Exeter, Birmingham and King's in London. Exeter's was the only one which attempted to link hospitals with local GP practices. The idea was to create an 'integrated patient record'. When anybody is admitted to hospital, particularly if it is as an emergency, the quicker their medical records are available the better. If the officer admitting the patient could just enter their name and bring up on screen the data kept in the bulging 'Lloyd George' envelopes at the surgery, together with details of previous admissions, home circumstances, allergies, it would save much duplication of effort. Systems Analysts were appointed who spent the next two years, 1970–2, investigating all the activities which take place in hospitals and Health Centres. This had never been done before and resulted in a 600-page document detailing how departments operated internally and how they linked with other parts of the NHS. From 1972 the DHSS funded programmers to create the necessary software. A computer was installed on the Wonford site in Bowmoor House (named after the house demolished for the new entrance from Barrack Road. The first Bowmoor House was built for the Head Attendant of Wonford House, and the gates intended to serve as the main entrance can still be seen at the corner of Barrack and Dryden Roads). Staff were recruited to run the system. It was designed to link up every GP practice and health centre in Devon with the hospital, but there was never enough funding to go beyond the pilot project, which linked Southernhay, PEOH and the Health Centres in Mount Pleasant and Ottery St Mary.

The Computer Project had a hexagon logo representing each individual patient and the six sections of records integrated by this process: the data held by one's GP; by the District Nurse; Outpatients; In-patients; ward nurses; path. lab. and pharmacy. In 1977 the Project

won a nation-wide competition run by the British Computer Society looking for the computer system 'most beneficial to mankind'. The prize was £1,000 and a glass statuette. When Jack Sparrow (Director 1970–83) retired in 1995 those who had worked on the Project were invited to a dinner in Taunton to use up the prize money. It had been the first computer centre in any UK hospital and possibly the first in the world. It was too far ahead of its time. The nurses had neither the time nor the training to enter information on the computers in the wards. In 1980 it was decided to run separate systems for the hospitals and the Health Centres, thus destroying the integrated nature of the project. By the time that its value was realised the team had

Retirement of Sister Ann Barter in 1986, with Dr Tony Daly and Prof. David Mattingly. She survived the transformation from Assistant Matron to Nursing Office i/c Medical Division. Prof. Mattingly paid tribute to her generation: 'The nurses trained the doctors while we trained them.'

Department of General Practice, Heavitree
Parish Church and Hippocratic plane tree.

moved to Bristol (in 1983). The hexagon
logo was taken over by the Exeter
Family Health Service Computer Project.

Noy Scott House was built on the
Wonford site in 1970 as the HQ of the
Devon, Exeter and Torbay Executive
Council, and named after Dr Steuart
Noy Scott to commemorate his years as
chairman of the local medical committee.

David Knowles was appointed chief
pharmacist in late 1971 to organize the
Pharmacy Department in the new hospital. He found the Southernhay premises appalling, and it seemed that
Wonford was going to replicate its worst
features. He adjusted the layout there
without taking up more space. When he
arrived, trained pharmacists were doing
menial tasks such as counting tablets.
He took on unskilled staff for this and
introduced an automated computer system which is still in existence. He agreed
with the Group Secretary to open at

Wonford eighteen months before the
rest of the hospital. The pharmacy there
also serves the Cottage Hospitals in
Lyme Regis, Dawlish, Teignmouth,
Axminster and others. The Southernhay
pharmacy remained open until the main
move of 1974. This computer system
was also far ahead of its time. It would
dispense the prescription, produce the
label, debit the stock, report to stock-
control system, reorder, issue invoice. If
there were two or more medicines, it
would check compatibility, indicate
pricing and make a drug utilization
print-out for wards and doctors.

In the seventies when the public were
taking package holidays and acquiring a
taste for foreign food Miss Theo
Churchard Catering Officer at the City
Hospital told the Express & Echo (22
January 1971) that, while varying the
menus, she always included potatoes,
gravy, custard – or the patients com-
plained. She was gradually offering foreign alternatives, such as ravioli. For the
nurses she even dared offer curry.

CHAPTER SEVEN

'A MATCHBOX ON A MUFFIN'

In late August 1968 the cricket ground at Barrack Road was bulldozed and Dr James Westwater once again cut a First Turf – this time for the new general hospital, 'We ask the doctors and nurses to practise twentieth-century medicine in nineteenth-century buildings – in Exeter in an eighteenth-century building...'

Dr George Stewart Smith quoted his words of 1964, that the pathology block had been put up as an act of faith, 'with a corridor to lead into a hospital we knew not when...' Groundwork now began. 77,000 cu. ft. of earth were removed, 17,250 cu. yds of concrete laid. Nobody gave a second thought to the fact that it was being poured straight on to soil that tests had shown to be unusually rich in alkali.

What would the new hospital be called? The Exonia Hospital? Should the constituent parts be called after the roads they stood on: Magdalen, Barrack, Heavitree Road? 'Wonford' was already the name of the mental hospital on the new site. Really, the hospital's name should continue to reflect the fact that it served Exeter and the greater part of Devon, so 'Devon and Exeter' would be ideal. But would the Queen allow the 'Royal' to be transferred?

In mid-March 1970 the Management Committee announced that as soon as the foundation stone was laid in July the names would be RD&E (Southernhay), RD&E (Heavitree) for City Hospital, and RD&E (Wonford) for the new district general hospital. The Queen had approved the retention of 'Royal'. As a local historian I find it unfortunate that the name 'Heavitree', where the hospital stands, right next to Heavitree Church,

The 1974 hospital from the grounds of Wonford House.

was not given to the main hospital. Instead, on the 'What's the nearest road?' principle, the name was given to City, which is not even in the parish of Heavitree. So, for years, mention of RD&E (Heavitree) led to the question: 'You mean City? Or the one at Heavitree?'

On 1 July, 300 gathered, including Mayor and Mayoress, Sheriff and wife, to watch the foundation stone being laid. Dr George Stewart Smith used a ceremonial trowel and mallet which had been 'used in similar ceremonies by four generations of royalty, from Queen Victoria to Queen Elizabeth the Queen Mother, but in other cities, Mr Peter le Fleming, Group Secretary of the Exeter and Mid-Devon Hospital Management Committee, said that the three general hospitals in the city, whose work was complementary, would now have the same title. He said the name was:

a debt to the past and a responsibility to the future ... It is appropriate for us to remember today the generous benefactors of the past and the devoted work of the staff throughout all these years and to accept these as an inspiration for the future.

Enoch Powell's Hospital Plan of 1962 had not yet been fully realized. The plan was reviewed in 1969. Current thinking was that District General Hospitals should be larger, serving populations of 200,000 to 300,000. Consultants would then not feel so isolated. When the replacement RD&E was being planned in the 1960s the Ministry of Health did not have a standard recommended design. There were guidelines, e.g. one carparking space per bed. Exeter consultants had regular meetings over many years planning their dream hospital. The budget was £8,000,000, so as in 1741 the brief was to make every pound work. The first District General Hospital built since the

Second World War was Treliske in Truro. Money had become tighter since then. Treliske was said to have been equipped to the standard of a really good house, with superior door fittings and floor finish. In comparison, Wonford would be more like a council house.

The planning group was made up of representatives of the consultants and management, and Matron Furze to speak on behalf of the nurses. An architect sat in on the group meetings and made instant sketches of possible designs. Some members of the group visited hospitals in Scandinavia looking for successful ideas. One system was rejected as it was too much like a conveyor belt: on arrival a patient was stripped and put in a kind of shroud and laid on a bed that then became their 'home'; their possessions were put in a carrier under the bed. They went in that bed to the ward, to X-ray, to the theatre... Matron was sent to look at hospitals in Northern Ireland.

The planning group eventually decided on a seven-storey tower-block of wards standing on a two-storey podium. It is called in the trade 'a matchbox on a muffin'. Inside the tower the layout was what is called 'race-track' – services and the nurses' stations in the middle, rooms on the outside with picture windows. No more Nightingale wards – there would be six-bed bays plus some single rooms. A ward could be mixed, one bay male, one bay female. This created a flexible arrangement. An innovation was a day-room for every ward, supplied with all services, for use as a ward during redecoration. Because of the vertical design (wards piled on top of each other with a liftshaft in the middle and stairs each end), the area allotted to circulation was only one tenth of the total. On the other hand, the corridors on each floor were wide, in case they had to hold extra beds after a nuclear attack.

The question was asked, should there

be windows in the operating theatres? It was unfashionable to have any and air-conditioning was easier to control. But the surgeons insisted that it was essential for the health of the staff who would be spending all day in the theatres to have a view of the outside world.

Advances in medicine necessitated a coronary care unit, an enlarged cardiology department, a separate department of anaesthetics, and improved accommodation for the blood transfusion service. Dr Hadden designed a state-of-the-art radiotherapy department. Management and the Ministry of Health insisted that the restaurant should be open to the public and all the staff, with not even one private table reserved for the consultants.

A Scandinavian-style residential village for 260 people in T-shaped 3-storey red-brick blocks of flats was built in 1973–4 on a knoll above Bovemoors Lane, looking across to a ridge of green fields, to attract young doctors to come to Exeter. The blocks were named after the early inspiration for nursing and ward-design (Nightingale), the benefactor of 1741 (Tuckfield) and some of Exeter's eminent eighteenth-century and nineteenth-century doctors (Dicker, John Patch, Sheldon, Haddy James, Glass, Baker, Barnes, William Budd, Shapter, Russell Coombe). This land had previously been the farm for Wonford House, providing fruit and vegetables. The surplus had been taken by horse and cart to sell in Higher Market.

In 1971 the new Conservative government addressed once again the perpetual paradox of accountability, the intrinsic impossibility of doing the very best for each patient while staying within cash limits. Keith Joseph took advice from a team of management consultants. A new structure was introduced on 1 April 1974 by which time there was a new Labour government. The Daily Mirror said the new 'streamlined NHS' had gone 'management-mad'. The con-

cept was 'maximum delegation downward, maximum accountability upward'. Hospital Management Committees were abolished. The 14 Regional Health Boards were re-named Regional Health Authorities. Devon came under the South Western RHA. Ninety new 'Area Health Authorities' would have geographical boundaries corresponding to the redrawn county boundaries. It was hoped that this would enable hospitals, GPs and local authority health services to cooperate, despite their continuing distrust of (respectively) local 'interference' in the hospitals, and bureaucratic 'interference' in clinical decisions or government 'interference' in local matters. The restructuring added another administrative layer; the county-shape Area Health Authorities were too large; things needed to be decided at district level, that is, the level of each District General Hospital. So within Devon there were established four district committees: North Devon, Exeter, Torbay and Plymouth, each with a catchment area of about a quarter of a million people. These 'management teams' each consisted of an administrator, a treasurer, a consultant, a general practitioner, a community physician and a nurse, with collective authority to take decisions involving spending a few thousand pounds without having to go to the Area Health Authority. Each district had a capital project team which met monthly. Each Area Health Authority could make decisions which involved spending up to about £1,000,000. But the Regional Health Authority was responsible for major capital works over £100,000. And at the top of the pyramid the total NHS budget of three billion a year was accountable by the current Minister of Health, Mrs Barbara Castle.

By June 1974 the new Regional Health Authority found it had inherited a £30,000 overspend. It had expected a £250,000 underspend and suspected that

Pathology block, and 1974 hospital on its extensive two-story podium.

the outgoing Boards had just stopped bothering. This was the first time that the NHS had been in the red, and this was ironic, because it was the first year that any 'underspend' would have been allowed to be carried forward.

Outside the tight budgeting at every level there was plenty of room for charitable fund-raising. In mid-April 1974, Bob Parker, manager of the ABC Cinema in Exeter, raised enough money in fifteen days for an American instrument to be bought for operations on the retina. There was only one such already in the UK, at Moorfields Hospital in London. By the following January, another appeal by Bob Parker had raised enough money to buy a pneumotonograph for the detection and cure of glaucoma. And in September 1975 he was able to give the Eye Infirmary a minute microphone and colour TV monitor for students to watch operations.

The Secretary of State Keith Joseph had appointed as chair of the Devon Area Health Authority a retired colonial administrator, Sir Derek Jakeway. The HQ was in the new office block by Exe Bridge, Renslade House. The committee was made up of representatives of local government, trade unions, the university and the healthcare professions.

David King became Exeter's new District Health Administrator. He had read sociology at Exeter University. He calculated that the Exeter area hospitals cost £12 million pa, but in the new premises at Wonford another million pa would be needed. The premises would be bigger. Where Southernhay had four X-ray diagnostic rooms Wonford would have eight. Instead of three operating theatres there would be eight, plus an accident theatre and a plaster theatre. Instead of the 30-bed Nightingale wards at Southernhay there would be 6-bed units plus singles, and a 10-bed day-case unit. 128 more beds in fact, making a total of 460. One hundred extra nurses would also be needed.

In the run-up to the great move in

1974, Southernhay was allowed to run down, the cubicle curtains were in shreds, hardly any new patients were admitted so that they would not have to be moved, and those that were left were put into a mixed ward as there were so few of them.

There was a sale of surplus damaged stores. Torn muslin shrouds sold quickly for jelly bags.

The move to Wonford was delayed from June/July to November 1973 and then to March 1974. There were difficulties in completing the new X-ray department. Complex equipment had become obsolete since it was first ordered. Because of the Three Day Week and shortage of steel, the new beds were not delivered and old ones had to be brought from Southernhay, and there was a wait for theatre instruments for ENT surgery. The old equipment from Southernhay could not be used in this case because of a different sterilizing technique. Not enough cleaners could be recruited to travel out of town, despite newspaper appeals describing the built-in shine of the floors and the absence of corners to collect dust. For light cleaning and carrying meal trays, wearing turquoise overalls and a checked apron, $53^{1/2}$p an hour was offered. For a fortnight in March the hospital opened to hundreds of sightseers. At the end of April a new bus route began to serve Barrack Road from Paris Street, approximately every 20 minutes. This improved access for patients, visitors and potential cleaners.

Nurses had grievances, particularly in relation to pay. They did not come out on strike, or work to rule, but on 28 May 1974 200 from Exeter, Honiton and Tiverton marched silently from Southernhay to the Devon Health Area HQ in Renslade House. They carried placards reading 'Are you sick? So are we.' 'We Care for You. Do You Care for Us?' 'Help us to help you.' A petition was sent to Exeter's MP John Hannam

and the government set up an independent enquiry.

After decades of longing for new premises there were final regrets at what would be lost. Out-of-town there is cheap land and fresh air, and same-site facilities avoid duplication of services. But a city-centre location is convenient for emergencies, visitors and staff. RD&E, City and WEEI had all been within walking distance of the bus and rail stations, and near the shops and cinemas during the staff's time off. New Zealander A.D. Perrett, who was locum senior medical registrar in Southernhay August 1970–September 1971, wrote:

The old RD&E was something of a rabbit warren, inefficient externally but remarkably functional and pleasant to work in. It was a delight to be situated in the heart of the city but in a quiet square adjacent to the Cathedral.

Nothing was to be taken from Southernhay to Wonford unless officially approved and marked. Ward staff wanted to take their favourite items under cover of darkness. Beryl Raphael knew there would not be money for another Parker Knoll chair such as she had in her office and people marvelled to see it at Wonford: 'How did you manage to get that? Do you have a bad back?'

On 1 April 1974 the new hospital opened for out-patients only. It would take three months to transfer the whole set-up. WRVS volunteers were at hand to guide people along the shiny new corridors.

The Physiotherapy Department was one of the first to move. Half the staff had to stay behind to treat in-patients until the wards moved up too. The removal vans were loaded (against orders) with most of the old equipment, much of which outlived the new equipment supplied with the new department. Miss Anne Branscombe remembered:

We set off with some ceremony led by the Superintendent (myself) in my own car – flat tyre spoiled the effect and I arrived long after the van. The day went quite well once the electric kettle had been located and the plug changed – darkness fell – everyone felt worn out and 'lost' until in the distance could be heard the tinkling of music – the removal man came in with the last piece of equipment, the old piano on a trolley with one of the men playing it. We were open for business the next day.

The new Physiotherapy Department was larger (the gym would accommodate at least three of the old department) and it was of great value that it opened direct into the Occupational Therapy Department. This allowed close cooperation and a good rehabilitation service, but could have been much more effective with more staff. There could have been a quicker turn-over of beds for the elderly then. And in spite of Miss Branscombe's pleading at the planning stage that Physio needed to be near access for cars and ambulances the nearest put-down point was at the Out-patients entrance 100–200 yds away, with no porters to bring patients in chairs. They had to struggle along and rest before being treated.

The major move was accomplished in one weekend. Some patients were put in the Nuffield Hospital for one day. Little equipment needed to be moved at this point: new X-ray machines, operating tables and lamps were ready and waiting. Admission for surgery had ceased in Southernhay on 3 July. On 8 July the first in-patient at Wonford was greeted with a bouquet. The Accident and Emergency Departments moved on 14 July.

The new hospital had 430 beds for in-patients; hundreds of out-patients per day; 1,400 people working there, of which 800 were nursing staff. If the heating pipes had been laid end to end they would reach from Exeter to Plymouth. If the lifts were stacked up they would reach up a quarter of a mile. If the plastered partitions were put end to end it would be like a 10-ft high wall from Exeter to Torquay and back.

For the first time the Dermatology Department had a permanent home instead of having to move from one suite to another every day, as it had to in Southernhay. The fracture clinic was next to Out-patients, linked to two 'ideally designed' 30-bed unisex fracture wards and supporting theatres.

At last the pathology air-tube system came into use, whisking samples a few hundred yards and returning results while the operation was still taking place.

The 'temporary' unit at Hawkmoor which had served since 1955 transferred with its staff to Wonford, where it could enjoy the support of the path. lab., blood bank, anaesthetics and radiology. Trainees visited from Massachusetts General Hospital. Chemotherapy was abolishing the waiting-lists for TB and bronchiectasis. The unit's work now was surgery of the oesophagus and treating lung cancer.

The exterior of Wonford was thought ugly. After rain there were smudges on the concrete tower. (How much worse than merely unsightly this was to prove!) The cheap yellow bricks of the lower storeys were slow to weather. The main entrance was not easy to find. But all agreed at first that the inside was superb. The nurses were glad not to have to push heavy gas cylinders on trolleys. Instead there was piped oxygen and piped suction. In the wards, the patients had more privacy, though the nurses found it more difficult to observe how they were doing.

Each clinic had its own small waiting

The main reception area of the 1974 building.

area, which helped disperse the numbers waiting in the main reception area. The royal coat of arms was transferred from Southernhay. There was overnight accommodation for patients' relatives, and a light and restful chapel. The public had been asked to suggest ward names and the most popular idea was to call them after the many rivers of Devon. Level 9 had panoramic views of green hills, and a roof terrace. This level was mainly for radiotherapy patients, to give a boost to their spirits. Mr Lovegrove, head gardener for the Exe Vale hospitals, had already been working for a year on landscaping the surrounding 25 acres, scattering two and a half tons of grass seed, planting 250 standard trees and up to 2,500 flowering shrubs. A separate garden area outside the dining-room was dedicated to the memory of Dr Clifford Fuller, who had helped plan the new hospital over a quarter of a century.

One bonus was the 'Void'. As at Southernhay, the sloping site meant that there was space under the ground floor, but instead of installing a brewery etc. the builders of the 1970s had simply blocked it in and left no access. When the estate officers were allowed on site after completion they cut a hole into the Void and found enough room for the Incontinence Clinic, and more. They divided the space with breeze-blocks. David Knowles used a lot of this extra storage space for the distilled water, which he bought cheaply by the lorry-load.

While so many specialist departments settled happily into their new accommodation, the Eye Infirmary mourned the loss of its supporting services. It had depended on Southernhay for library, X-rays, pathology, and kitchen services. Doctors and nurses had also been accommodated there. But despite this the Eye Infirmary struggled on as a centre of excellence. Mr George Cantrell writes:

The Eye Infirmary was well to the fore in developing the modern technique of cataract surgery with plastic lens implants. This took 20 years

West of England Eye Infirmary, Magdalen Street, from the east.

to reach a reasonably useful level, and another 20 to go on to its present amazingly successful state. By 1983 when I left we were using lasers, ultrasound, sophisticated retinal photography and micro-surgery all undreamed of forty years previously.

WEEI was one of the first Eye Hospitals to use day case surgery for eye operations. Even in 1956 when I came here the routine in-patient times were ten days for a cataract, and a week for a squint op.

In October 1975 the National Union of Public Employees (NUPE) threatened industrial action unless private beds were phased out. Others believed that doctors would leave the NHS or even the UK if that happened. Of the 4,400 beds in the 33 hospitals in the Exeter Healthcare Area, only 16 were in fact private. There were none in RD&E (Wonford), two in RD&E (Heavitree), two in the Eye Infirmary, two in PEOH and 11 outside Exeter.

Once the honeymoon was over the complaints about Wonford began. The reception area was draughty if there was a gale. There should have been sliding doors at the entrance. The radiators leaked. Night after night there were calls about this to the Night Superintendent Beryl Raphael, finally totalling 200 faulty radiators. The windows would not be cleaned for two years because the gantries could not be used. There were no arrangements for evacuation in case of fire except that nurses would strap the patients to their mattresses and pull them downstairs holding a loop. The new catering system was called Ganymede. The 'cupbearer of the Gods' in the form of a ward-maid would hand an individual tray to each patient with the food they had chosen a day ahead. An advantage was that this gave a wider choice. Disadvantages: if someone was discharged the new occupant of their bed received their choice; Sister could no longer supervise whether the patient was choosing what was good for them, and whether they ate it all up. There was another problem with Ganymede. It was inflexible. For example, if a patient had had tests during the daytime and missed mealtime the night nurse could not make toast or boil an egg for them in the evening. The consultants did not like the public restaurant and tended to eat in the Postgraduate Medical Centre so as to be able to discuss cases privately, as they had in Southernhay. The junior doctors disliked having nothing but vending-machine food in the night. It took so long for nurses to reach the restaurant from the top wards that they were allowed to make tea and coffee on the wards.

The new, young Duchess of Gloucester was to have opened the new hospital on 15 May 1975 but hurt her ankle and her husband stood in for her. He dedicated the new sculptures in the Chapter House at the Cathedral and then drove to Wonford with Mayor Sam Honeywill. The Duke gestured to the tower block and joked that he was an architect himself. One of the consultants pointed out, 'This is the largest and most expensive building put up in this city since the cathedral and it is like a concrete German bunker.' Lunch for 500 was laid on in a marquee although the Duke had already moved on to the Devon County Show.

Back at Southerhay Arthur Kempe's chapel was deconsecrated by the Bishop and demolished, to allow access for development at the rear of the site. Only a vaulted lobby and connecting porch mark where it stood at the east end of the hospital. Development has in fact not taken place, and the rear is used for carparking only. Dr Hadden was sorry to see Elizabeth Ward demolished after putting so much effort into raising the money for it, designing it and running it as the first cobalt unit in the south-west. With the concrete 'maze' formed by the walls to stop radiation penetrating he thought it would have been worth keeping for an emergency shelter against nuclear attack.

The Regional Hospital Board had hoped to sell the Southernhay site (including the 1741 building, which is listed) and use the proceeds to add an extra 108-bed geriatric unit at Wonford. The premises had to be offered to other government departments and then to the local authority. If neither took it up they could sell to private developers. By 1977 the Area Health Authority had taken it for its pay office, accounts and audit sections, the Exeter Healthcare District administration, school dental clinic, Devon Chiropody workshop and school health clinics. The name was changed to Dean Clarke House and £125,000 was spent on the conversion. Former matron Ruth Furze marvelled at the expenditure – 'To think I tried for 11 years to get a hand-basin so that nurses could wash their hands when changing dressings...' The office move freed seven other buildings, some rented. Noy Scott House became available for the overflowing School of Nursing and Radiography, which had been designed to train 200 students and now had twice that number.

From 1963 Mr Caldwell, in collaboration with Drs Conn and Flack of the university's Physics Department had been working on the electronic control of incontinence, at first in a hut on the nurses' tennis court. After 1974 he discontinued general surgery to concentrate on this. 500 patients had already benefited when he received a NHS grant in 1977 for further research.

In the 1980s there was further restructuring of the NHS. The Area tier of management was excised in 1982. Districts became more autonomous. Sir George Younger welcomed the change: 'Decisions will be taken as near as possible to the point of delivery.' The next tier up was the Region, with a huge area, from Scilly to Cheltenham.

Devon Area Health Authority shut down on 31 March 1982. This saved the rent on five storeys of Renslade House. Murray French became Chairman of

Exeter Health Authority, with David King as Administrator. As part of the rearrangement a surplus of £500,000 was available to share out between the districts. A large part of Exeter's windfall was put towards the city's proposed new specialised home-nursing service for the terminally ill – Hospiscare. An appeal for this had been launched in the Guildhall in January 1982. It was a soaking wet night but the large numbers of people who came overflowed onto the High Street. The home-care service was able to begin in July 1982.

The Government then commissioned an inquiry by Roy Griffiths, Managing Director of Sainsbury's. His brief was to stop waste and inefficiency by clarifying individual responsibilities. His Report led to a dismantling of the top-heavy senior nursing structure. General man-agers replaced the consensus management teams. Griffiths also made the point in his report that most hospital problems stem from lack of money. But the Government was not going to provide any more money so each hospital had to try and generate income for itself.

On 10 September 1984 Princess Anne came by helicopter to County Hall and opened a new kidney unit at Wonford, which replaced the inadequate premises at Whipton. A public appeal had raised £475,000 towards the cost. For the 125 regular patients there were 11 rooms for in-patients, dialysis area, small operating theatre, lecture room, overnight accommodation, administrative offices and a workshop. It was named Sid Ward, which fitted in with the river-name theme but also related to the fund-raising logo, Sidney Kidney.

CHAPTER EIGHT
CRUMBLING FOUNDATIONS

Geoff Hingston was seconded from the Estates office to be Technical Officer for Wonford. The hospital had been up only two years and people were already commenting on the web of surface cracks – first like a cobweb, then 'Isle of Man' cracks. The cracks started exuding a white starchy gel. He could see that these were not just compression or intension cracks as the building settled down; it was something outside his experience. Then watching local TV one evening he saw an item about carparking in Plymouth and the multi-storey at Charles Cross. He could see the same sort of cracks there too. Next morning he rang Plymouth Health Authority and heard about Alkali Aggregate Reaction (AAR) – 'concrete cancer'. There was no cure, the concrete would crumble back into its constituent parts. They told him the world experts were a firm of consultants in London, Mott Hay & Anderson. 'Concrete cancer' had occurred extensively in Iceland during the Second World War, but was new to the UK. A partner of Mott Hay & Anderson set up a monitoring service at Wonford, reporting every quarter.

There had been a seam of silica in the sand quarry. This was reacting with the alkaline cement to form a gel. The chemical reaction causes the concrete to expand and push out the surface layers until they crumble and fall off. Condensation in the hospital kitchens could have started it off. On 7 July 1985 the Sunday Times reported:

On-site poured concrete, mixed and poured into moulds, often improperly mixed by unskilled workers, chemical reactions and impurities have led to cracking and crumbling in nearly all such structures since the early 70s.

Indeed, such cracking and crumbling was soon to be discovered in the Buddle Lane council houses in Exeter. One third of the UK's 4.6 million council houses were found to be affected in a 1981 survey. At Wonford, some of the aggregate had come from the seashore and some from inland sandpits.

At the same time there was a carbonization problem. The steel reinforcement bars which provided support to the uprights were not inserted according to specification. They were too close to the surface. Penetrating water was causing carbonization. Wet penetrates about two inches into concrete, or deeper in the south-west. The tower-block at Wonford was high and exposed. The SW side which faced most of the rain often had a quarter of an inch of water running down the surface. The site also had a high water-table.

Little bits of concrete the size of half-a-crown began falling from the lintels. A scaffolding tunnel was put up over the entrance to keep this 'rain' off the public. The roofs and seventeen courtyards were put out of bounds to staff unless wearing hard hats. Engineers monitored the cracking with pins and threads, measuring on a daily basis. A scientific paper about an occurrence in Finland in 1932 had said that AAR was active for about 12 years then petered out. At Wonford it was not petering out, it was increasing to nightmare proportions. It was not just unsightly mottling, not just gel exuding from surface cracks, but a sample plug extracted from the heart of the fabric showed cracking right through.

The RHA was still responsible for

major capital works. Each district had a capital projects team meeting monthly. The problem of concrete cancer would have taken all this team's time. A special monthly meeting was set up, with the regional architect and engineer, and assistant regional general manager Seignor McClelland and RHA member Cllr Jack Harris. They got permission to break open access to the foundations. Jack Harris will never forget the experience. The hospital rested on 540 pillars, each standing on a concrete pad 3 ft thick and about 15 ft square. They looked at three pads. There were deep cracks each side of the vertical pillars. The first one they examined was split right across and down in three different places. The thrust was being taken by the centre of the pad, not the 15 ft by 15 ft whole. The only members of the RHA major project group who examined the foundations with him were two former trades union officials. They were used to scrutinizing wording and urged him to look at the small print in the builders' contract and go to arbitration.

The outer structure was breaking up. How quickly would the 'cancer' travel through the foundations? In five years? Ten years? As soon as it had been identified in the uprights it began to accelerate there – cobwebs, then 'Isle of Man' then actual splits. The block was not a single tower but three linked sections. The most sensitive area was the central core with the lift shafts. Most of the cracking was here, and this was where it could do most damage. The central section only had to shift 10 mm out of true to fracture all the piping and wiring. As Jack Harris said, 'It will be too late when the operating tables start sliding across the floor.' Engineers cut off a two-storey high supporting column at the entrance to the Radiotherapy Department, put in a girder and inserted a jack to thrust it down. Nothing happened. Perhaps it was safe to go on using the hospital? The decision to rebuild would be a huge

responsibility. There was no spare money at district level. There was no spare money at regional level. They could not afford to demolish and rebuild unless they were certain that there was no alternative. It had been built for £7m. it would take at least £45m to replace. Could it be saved and patched up while the whole hospital moved out temporarily? Could a plastic coating halt the reaction by stopping the wet getting in? This had been tried in Australia but without success – on the contrary, the reaction speeded up when air was excluded. Plymouth had put straps round parts of its viaduct. A viaduct or carpark is one thing; a nine-storey hospital has a greater potential for tragedy. Exeter had other structures from 1969 cracking: the incinerator at Marsh Barton, the Exe Bridges (although here the problem was static, perhaps because it was continually wet).

Two government officials came to the monthly meetings which were held in the Postgraduate Medical Centre opposite the tower block. Afterwards they and other members sat in the car and looked at the tall building. 'We've got to decide whether to spend all that money.' One day as they sat there a lateral beam about three storeys up began to swing loose. They realised they would have to rebuild and the money would have to come from central government. Jack Harris got hold of the Devon MPs whose constituencies were served by the RD&E. They met one Saturday morning. Robin Maxwell-Hyslop, MP for Tiverton, was elected chair, as the senior member present at the meeting. He suggested looking at the contract to see how long the builders, Higgs & Hill, were liable. Things speeded up. They found that the twelve-year guarantee had only a fortnight to run. The Mott Hay & Anderson man took the MPs on a tour of the exterior and the interior, up scaffolding and down into the depths. The group asked Maxwell-Hyslop to

It's your NHS – find out how it's getting on...

The NHS Performance Guide 1994–95

RAISING THE STANDARD

The NHS never stands still

The NHS is changing all the time. Now, for the second year, we're publishing information which shows you how your local health services match up against the rest.

All NHS organisations keep records of just how well – or how badly – they are doing their job. The *NHS Performance Guide* brings together the results that concern people most.

The new NHS Performance Guide for 1994–95

To find out what the Guide says about **your** local services, call the Health Information Service on 0800 66 55 44.

What the figures can tell you

The figures show how all NHS Trusts and hospitals in England are performing on:

- how quickly you might get seen in an outpatient department

- the speed of assessing accident and emergency patients

- whether operations are arranged quickly after a last-minute cancellation

- allowing patients to have operations without having to stay in hospital overnight

- how quickly you could be admitted for treatment if you're a non-emergency patient

- how long you might have to wait for your first outpatient appointment.

The figures also show how quickly ambulances arrive in different areas, and the percentage of GPs who have a practice charter.

How this information can help

You and your family doctor can use the figures to decide where you can get the best health care.

Under the Citizen's Charter initiative, you have the right to know how **all** public services perform. The *NHS Performance Guide* enables you to check how well the NHS Trusts, hospitals and ambulance services near you are doing their job.

Your Patient's Charter rights

The Patient's Charter has helped to improve the service that the NHS gives – from shorter waiting lists with fewer people on them to more and better information.

The Charter sets out your rights and the standards the NHS should meet in caring for you:

- the healthcare you should have access to
- the way you should be treated by medical staff
- the choices you're entitled to during your care
- and targets for prompt service.

It also tells you what information you can expect – about the NHS in general, about your local services in particular, and about the treatment you are receiving.

How you can help the NHS

Remember, you can help the NHS improve its services by using them responsibly; so please remember to:

- let us know as soon as possible if you cannot keep an appointment. This will help us to see someone else instead;

- tell your doctor or hospital if you change your name, address or telephone number;

- return equipment such as wheelchairs, crutches, walking sticks or frames when you no longer need them so that they can be used by other patients;

- give us your comments and suggestions – so that we can improve services wherever possible;

- give blood regularly – call 0345 711711 (local call charge) to find out about how to give blood in your own neighbourhood;

- enter your name on the NHS Organ Donor Register by completing the registration form available from post offices, pharmacists, GP surgeries or by ringing Freephone 0800 555 777, and carry an Organ Donor Card. Always discuss your wishes with your relatives;

- remember that you benefit if your GP has a good night's sleep, so please only call your doctor out at night if it cannot wait until the next day;

- use the emergency ambulance services responsibly and call 999 only in emergencies.

To find out more about how your local health services are performing

Call the Health Information Service free on:

0800 66 55 44

The Health Information Service lines are open from at least 10 am to 5 pm Monday to Friday.

You can also call for information about health and health care generally. Your call will be answered by someone who has the facts. It's their job to help you.

For a copy of the *NHS Performance Guide*, ring 0800 555 777. For further copies of this leaflet write to: BAPS, Health Publications Unit, Storage and Distribution Centre, No 2 Site, Heywood Stores, Manchester Road, Heywood, LANCS OL10 2PZ. © Crown Copyright. Produced by Department of Health. G72/002 2992 1RP 100k July 95. LTL95.

make an appointment to see the Prime Minister, Margaret Thatcher. He often got good results by sending a preliminary letter – 'My dear Margaret, I am approaching you as First Lord of the Treasury...' (the Chancellor of the Exchequer being technically the Second Lord). They met on the Tuesday afternoon, she picked up the telephone and ordered the Treasury to release £40 million to the South West Region for the reprovision of Wonford. Jack Harris regards this as a demonstration of the power of the people's vote: the local MPs saw the evidence, took it to the PM and £40 million was released. The Health and Social Services Secretary Norman Fowler announced it at the end of July 1986: a grant of £40 million towards a £50 million rebuild. The first £5 million was allocated for 1988–9. The Region must find the shortfall by selling its newly vacated mental hospitals at Digby and Exminster and elsewhere.

Jack Harris persuaded the Regional Health Authority (RHA) to issue a High Court Writ against the builders only days before the crucial action would have become 'out of time'. Higgs & Hill engaged barristers and so did the RHA. To the first charge that they ought to have foreseen the 'concrete cancer' problem they successfully pleaded that it had been an unknown phenomenon. They offered to put things right for £3 million rather than pay out £6 million compensation. The second charge was 'Failure to comply with specifications'. They had contracted to use materials that would last for 60 years and the authority would have only 15 years' use of the building. The floor screed had not been the traditional mix of cement and sand and it was rising. The whole building was moving. The way the concrete walls were put in was faulty – boarded, concrete mixed on site, poured in, reinforcement rods forced in; and the timings of the pourings: do a wall so far, leave it, come back later with a different mix; also the steel was badly inserted; also they had not used the specified wall ties but cheap butterfly ties which were not strong enough to hold the walls together. The two leading barristers representing Higgs & Hill came to SW Region, said that they realized that they would lose and asked for time to think before the adjudication. They finally offered a settlement.

Other buildings at Wonford were found to suffer from crumbling concrete: the older part of the PGMC, the old Renal Department and some of the laundry and estate buildings.

Mott Hay & Anderson advised how to go about the demolition with minimum dust and noise. They suggested diamond cutters and huge cranes to lift out the slabs one by one as they were cut.

In May 1985 Stewart Smith House was added to the Residential Village to serve as a hostel for 18 undergraduate medical students from Bristol on attachment here. It was declared open jointly by the Vice-Chancellor of Exeter University David Harrison – (the University had provided the £200,000 capital costs) – and Murray French – (the Exeter Health Authority were paying the running costs). It was named after the Consultant Pathologist 1949–67 who had been instrumental in developing the new hospital services and medical education in Exeter.

In November 1985 no-smoking areas were designated in the hospitals. On Ash Wednesday 1989 Action for Smoking and Health (ASH) planted a weeping ash-tree near Church Lane as a reminder of the dangers of smoking.

Exeter won an accolade in 1986 when its 'Psychological Care project' was made the prototype for the rest of Britain. Dr Keith Nichols had trained nurses to give information in the best way. Then in July 1989 Government reports advised other authorities to follow Exeter's example in rehabilitation for the elderly, continence advice and pioneering pharmacy services. In May 1990 Dr Terry Feest and his team won an award for their videos of information for kidney patients.

However, at the same time, the RD&E was beset by a series of unfortunate incidents. In April 1988 a surgeon who had been a mission doctor in Africa died of AIDS. The risk to his patients was minimal but it was the first such occurrence and it generated great media interest. Not long after, it was discovered that a radiotherapy machine had been wrongly calibrated. In a six-month period February to July 1988 it had been giving doses 25% higher than prescribed. Consultants do vary in the doses they prescribe. A palliative dose may be small, and a quarter of a small amount is not very much. But an extra 25% on a large dose could be dangerous. About one hundred patients claimed compensation.

On a happier note soon after Kate Caldwell was appointed as Director of Midwifery in 1990, a team midwifery scheme for midwifery care was introduced in the maternity department. Three teams of staff care for a third of the mothers each. The mothers become closely involved with their own team, named 'Blue', 'Yellow' and 'Green', both

in the hospital and the attached teams in the community. This has increased consistency in advice and support and brought some improvement in continuity of care and carer. Several other maternity departments have adopted Exeter's approach as it has been found to be very successful. The team philosophy has also included a close partnership with the innovative neonatal unit and the gynaecology ward.

Another welcome advance was made by Hospiscare. A hospice is defined as 'a resting place for weary travellers'. In 1982 the charity had been able to pay for two nurses to visit patients or give advice by telephone. In 1989 a site became available on the corner of Dryden Road where a real Hospice could be built if enough money were raised. To provide the twelve beds which had been the norm in the equivalent medieval foundations, and a day centre for a further twelve, for respite and pain control, £1,600,000 was needed, and £180,000 running costs. Dr John Searle led a vigorous campaign. By April 1990 £500,000 had been raised and council leader Chester Long handed over the first of four payments of £25,000 pledged by the city. The Hospice opened in 1992, facing south towards hills and shady trees.

CHAPTER NINE

THE NEW HOSPITAL

The usual gestation period of a major hospital is ten years. Exeter could not wait that long. The structural engineers recommended that the tower should be vacated soon after 1990 although the podium could be used for a few years longer. It was 1985 when the Department of Health agreed in principle that a new hospital was needed. Within three and a half years the foundations were underway, after more than a hundred meetings of a special steering group and countless meetings about the finer details. Manager David King had been delighted by the challenge: 'Let's do it better this time!' At first he had the group meet every Friday lunchtime at Wonford to get senior physicians and nurses to think about new flexible approaches to healthcare. He plucked David Knowles from the pharmacy to be secretary (and later full-time General

Manager). He himself was chair. The others were mainly senior hospital consultants namely Mr Patrick Beasley, Dr Matthew James, Dr Brian Kirby, Mr Andrew Knox, Dr Anthony Nicholls, Dr Christopher Rowland and Dr John Tripp – no architects or engineers until much later. They were dreaming up the District General Hospital of the 21st century. They produced a report listing their ideal facilities: surgical wards directly opposite theatres; Accident & Emergency near Intensive Care (ITU); the eye ward alongside day care; children's Bramble Ward alongside children's Out-patients, Ear Nose & Throat (ENT) and other relevant units. The academic staff needed office accommodation near each other for easy communi-

Main entrance of the new hospital 1992.

cation. Teachers needed a centre for large groups and small teaching rooms near the wards. Ideally the dining facilities for all medical staff (hospital and GPs) should have a 'social centre' where informal professional discussion would be possible. Instead of the traditional wards, theatres and separate Out-patients they wanted each team to have ward, theatre and Out-patients attached. This would make sense for Cardiology, Radiotherapy, Ophthalmology, ENT and Dental departments.

The Region said they could not afford such a dream hospital. David King persisted. He argued that the new building would not have such high maintenance costs. Services would be infinitely more efficient on one site instead of being separated as widely as Heavitree, Honeylands, WEEI, Newcourt and PEOH.

Instead of specialized departments in separate buildings, all the departments could share diagnostic and operating facilities. The anaesthetists believed that High Dependency Care, Coronary Care, Intensive Care, Special Baby Unit and Post-Transplant could usefully be near each other, equipment could be pooled and nurses could help each other out. Thoracic medicine was keen to be more closely associated with the general medical admitting arrangements. At the time they had separate 24-hour admitting cover. Geriatrics wanted improved links with general medicine and specialities and diagnostic facilities.

It would make sense for Dieticians, Clinical Psychologists and Medical Social Workers to be near Out-patients, together with Physiotherapy, Speech Therapy and Occupational Therapy. The latter three would settle for smaller premises but extra space at ward level. A 'forward waiting area' by each operating theatre would avoid delay in fetching patients from the wards. A governing factor was that reprovision of each hospital service must be at the previous

level unless there was good reason to raise it. It was possible to show that work was increasing greatly in the Fracture Clinic, Cardiology, the Sexually Transmitted Diseases Clinic and in Radiology. The local planning group was allowed 'its flight of fancy'. Then the officers of Region had to go through the mundane processes, the Option Appraisal, setting out the problem, the proposal, costing the 'Do nothing' option or of building somewhere different, or demolishing and building on the same site. Theoretically the tower could be repaired but would have to be evacuated for 4–5 years. Could the hospital be evacuated to the empty mental hospital at Exminster for those years? No – the cost of adapting those premises would be £25 million wasted.

The only solution was to build afresh.

Michael Huscroft, of the Region's Planning Department, and Nigel Walsh, who had been the RD&E's general administrator, were charged with the detailed planning work and local negotiations, alongside architects Dick Venn and Ivan Wiggam, and members of the Steering Group. The major constraint on the plan was that the new hospital had to be built while the old one was still standing and in use and occupying some of the area which would eventually be needed for the new building. In the 1970s a large area of the grounds had been left as a green 'buffer' round Wonford House, with respect to its seniority and its patients' need for peace and quiet. The new hospital would need to be slotted in on this very buffer zone. It is unlikely that psychiatric patients will be accommodated in Wonford House much longer, so the new plans were allowed to encroach onto its rear territory. Trees were planted as a screen.

The Department of Health approved Phase One – to build replacements for the wards in the tower. The Department had a preferred design, the 'Nucleus'. It consists of cruciform units of back-to-

back wards sharing an entry corridor. Members of the Steering Group visited examples of this type of design in Maidstone and Bridgend.

Members of the Wonford Rebuild Steering Group on a site visit in the Summer of 1989.

The 1970s tower had often been criticised for spoiling the sky-line. This time low-rise was chosen. Exeter is not a city of sky-scrapers. The Nucleus plan has a low risk of fire; each block can be isolated and evacuated to its neighbour. Architect Dick Venn presented his plans to the City Council. They were won over by the pleasant proportions of Venn's plan, the local brick (instead of the metal cladding used on Nucleus by other authorities) and the pitched grey roofs which were designed to harmonise with the slate roofs of Wonford House.

The rebuild was about 'function for function' not 'area for area'. Every clinician wanted to retain at least the same square footage, but the Department of Health had issued revised space specifications since the 1970s. The theatres in the tower had been small. The new ones would be smaller because the technology is more compact.

The new hospital is what estate agents call 'deceptively spacious' – it is actually smaller than its predecessor. Those endless corridors in fact add up to a smaller total of circulation area. The group argued successfully for having the basic 'template' extended by one bay at the entrance to each ward to provide room for doctors' offices and teaching and research rooms.

Phase One and Two were costed at £53–55 million. £40 million had been allocated to the Region by the Department of Health. The Region would have to find the shortfall by jiggling its whole capital works programme. The £23,000,000 Phase One was built in 1991–2. Seven blocks replaced all the wards from the tower. Accident & Emergency and Outpatients remained in the podium, with linking corridors to the new hospital. The old hospital had had a fund-raising bookshop but the new has a shopping mall, with minimarket, bookshop, florist and charity shop, and a Patients' Information Centre. This is the only part of the hospital completely designed for local requirements. Above it are administrative offices and bedrooms for doctors on call and relatives staying overnight.

Directly to the right of the main reception desk is the West of England Eye Unit, moved at last from Magdalen Street. With more day surgery fewer beds are needed. The ward is named after Parker's Well, the pure spring at the corner of Matford Lane where locals would bathe their eyes. The Hospital League of Friends raised £150,000 in an 'Eyes Right' appeal in 1991 for a second operating theatre and a support unit for day-case surgery for 1,000 extra cataract operations a year, 60% as day cases.

Phase One admitted its first patients in June 1992. Work went straight on with Phase Two from mid-1992 to 1995, at an eventual cost of £45 million.

The new hospital is on a human scale. In the tower block people used the lifts and seldom met. Now on the long 'street' on each floor they meet and greet. It has been described as 'villages in a city'. Unlike its rather monochrome predecessor, it is decorated in a range of pleasant colours and the corridors are carpeted.

Yet another adjustment to the NHS replaced direct budget allocations with a series of contracts between budget-holding 'purchasers' and service providers. 'The money will follow the patient.' The RD&E was awarded the status of an NHS Trust under the chairmanship of Dame Margaret Turner Warwick from 1 April 1993. Buckingham Palace gave permission for it to be called the Royal Devon & Exeter Healthcare Trust. As at the beginning, it has to balance the books by itself now – there is no Region to jiggle the accounts and bale it out. To bring the statistics up to date, the yearly hospital expenditure in 1998 is about £100,000,000.

On 17 March 1994 the Duchess of Kent officially opened the new building. An enthusiastic throng welcomed her into the new Concourse with the sunshine streaming in. The Duchess then toured the hospital before performing the opening ceromony. This was just one part of a day of Celebration of 250 Years of Healthcare in Exeter which included an exhibition at the Cathedral Chapter House, a Civic Luncheon and a Service of Thanksgiving in the Cathedral.

On 23 February 1996 the actress, Susan Hampshire, a vice-president of the International Tree Foundation, interrupted a week on the stage in North Devon to plant a Luccombe Oak near the Barrack Road entry. She also inspected other trees given by the society above Church Lane.

That same month, pharmacy and kitchen staff were the last to vacate the 1970s building and demolition could begin. Aid worker Robert Gibbing salvaged outdated X-ray equipment and anything else that could be used in Romania. The beds were completely worn out, some being the old ones fetched from Southernhay when the new ones did not arrive in 1974. The fittings of the operating theatres were plumbed in and could not be recycled. The rest went to scrap merchants. Police used the ruins to train dogs.

Clyst and Creedy Wards were retained. They were ground-floor and had not been built until 1984 so it was hoped that they were safe. At its north end the new building was only two metres away from the tower which was to be demolished. The 120-ft high 9-storey block had to be taken down without explosion and with minimal noise and dust. It was done carefully over 40 weeks. First it was covered with scaffolding and monoflex sheeting. A small mechanical crusher was hoisted into the roof to work down to level four or five. Then larger machines could be brought in. As panels were taken off the ceilings

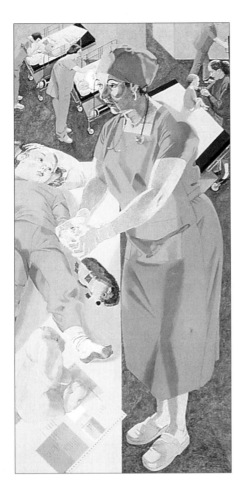

Above: 1849 print of Southernhay by Angel Hays.
Top: A water colour from Tony Foster's River Journey project.
Left: One of Ivy Smith's paintings near the shops.

cracks in the floors were revealed. The foundations looked as if there had been explosions inside the concrete.

In February 1997 Dr John Tooke and his team in the Department of Diabetes and Vascular Medicine won The Queen's Anniversary Award for outstanding excellence in research. There has been a blossoming of research initiatives and achievements, far more than can be listed here.

The new Accident and Emergency (A&E) department had been designed to deal with 40,000 patients a year. By September 1997 it was treating about 60,000, including Saturday sports injuries and holiday-makers involved in road crashes. The Air Ambulance was also bringing in casualties. The League of Friends launched an appeal for £220,000 to provide better resuscitation

facilities, a larger waiting-room with mother-and-baby facilities, and a bereavement room.

The new Princess Elizabeth Orthopaedic Centre (PEOC) opened in October 1997 at a cost of £11 million. Now the other services are literally just down the corridor: three elective orthopaedic wards, a trauma ward, four operating theatres (two Ultra Clean) to carry out 3,000 operations pa, outpatient and therapy areas to treat 15,000 pa, a hydrotherapy pool. An appeal by Exeter Princess Elizabeth Research and Training (EXPERT) raised £250,000 for an 80-seat lecture theatre, two research labs and an anatomy lab.

The ward-names commemorate the long-serving matron, Miss Knapp, and surgeons Capener, Durbin and Dyball.

The PEOH had always been proud of its six flagpoles, flying the Union Jack; its own blue and white badge with cross and white rose; the Belgian flag because of a long-standing training arrangement

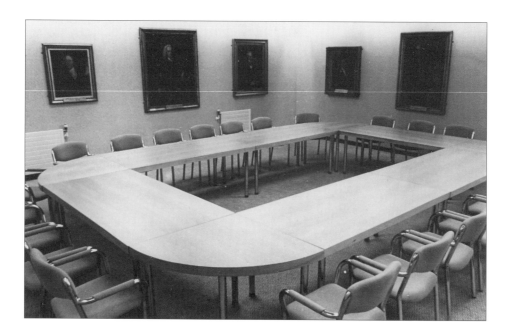

with Louvain; and the flags of current trainees from India, Pakistan and Africa. The Centre is pleased to have six new flagpoles at its entrance.

On the walls of the hospital stairways and corridors many poems, photographs and paintings cheer and interest passers by. The RHA began to sponsor an arts project in 1992. Some paintings are on loan but many were specially commissioned: Paul Spooner's 'Keep Fit' automaton in the reception area, Pat Johns' large tapestry of the Exe Estuary by the main entrance, Ivy Smith's scenes of hospital life by the shops and Vanessa Robertson's woven hangings in the chapel. Kate Malone's water feature with ceramic fish decorates the courtyard of Bramble Ward. In 1997 the National Lottery awarded £405,000 for further commissions. The PEOC already has an artistically enhanced atrium, including a hanging sculpture and floor designs by Ray Smith.

Nigel Walsh, Director of Planning, reflects:

'From the time we first set out to plan the replacement for the 1970s RD&E (Wonford) building, we envisaged the eventual transfer and integration of services from RD&E (Heavitree). These were primarily Maternity, Gynaecology, Neonatology and Elderly Care. In 1993 there was a strategic review which confirmed that the achievement of future clinical and financial objectives depended largely on completing the consolidation of services on a single site at Wonford.

'The opening of the new Princess Elizabeth Orthopaedic Centre, Phase Three, in October 1997 left only the transfer of Heavitree to complete the 'jigsaw', as Phase Four. In fact Orthopaedic services had to be put ahead of Heavitree in the plan owing to the devolution of Orthopaedics and the establishment of local services particularly in Torbay.

'Not surprisingly, plans for re-siting the Heavitree services focus on the area of the Wonford site left vacant after the demolition and removal of the diseased old building and its foundations. People tend to forget that one of the main reasons for the layout of the new hospital is

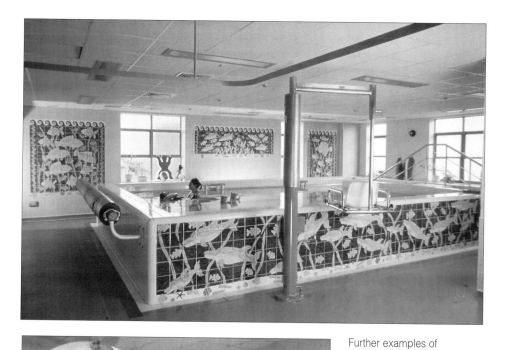

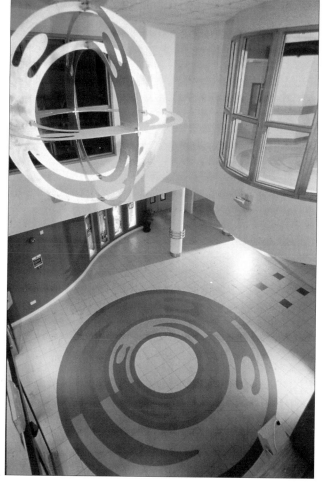

Further examples of commissions by Exeter Health Care Arts.
Above: PEOC hydrotherapy pool with ceramic designs by Reptile.
Left: PEOC main entrance; complementary hanging scuplture and floor design by Ray Smith

Opposite above: The Board Room of the 1990s with some of the portraits from Southernhay.

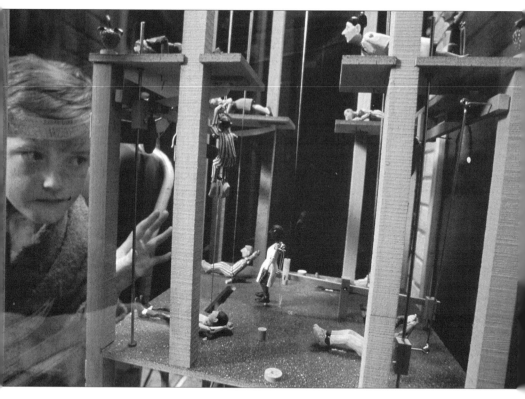

Above: Paul Spooner's Keep Fit Machine

Right Above: Bramble Ward courtyard, Kate Malone's ceramic fish tank.
Right below: The light and peaceful chapel. Architect Ivan Wiggam. Dedicated in November 1993 by the
Rt. Revd Hewlett Thompson, Bishop of Exeter, with hospital chaplains, Revd David Walford (Anglican),
Revd Patrick Conlon (RC), Revd Kenneth Hext (Methodist) and Revd Derek Keenan (Baptist).

Below: Meg Surrey's Theatre Trail.

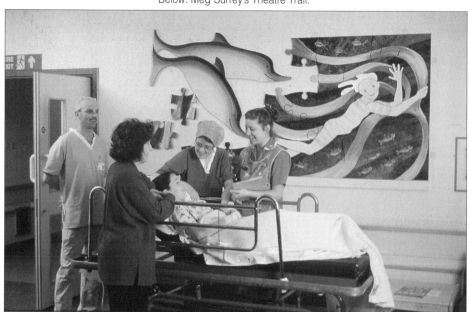

that it had to be fitted around the old one and that the wards in the first phase had to be linked with the old building while the second phase was in construction. So, for example, although we have a very good geographical relationship between the surgical wards, operating theatres and emergency departments, the Main Entrance is away from the road and at a distance from car parks and the Accident and Emergency Department itself is effectively round the back of the building.

In Phase Four we hope not only to integrate the Heavitree services, but also to build a new main entrance to the whole hospital facing Barrack Road and easy access to car parks at that end of the site.'

When the Maternity Unit moves from Gladstone Road it will have its related specialized departments close at hand

(Obstetrics, Gynaecology, Neonatology) but there will be no need to duplicate the general services such as operating theatres and day-care units.

So, at the end of our tale, a brand-new sprawling palace on an out-of-town ridgeway is housing the services formerly provided by the WEEI, PEOH, the hospitals of 1741 and 1974, and those of RD&E Heavitree soon, and maybe eventually Honeylands.

There has not been space in these pages to mention all the advances in treatment particulaly over the last 20 years, all the changes in professional training, all the good works of fundraisers. The examples given, of dedication and excellence and dogged perseverance, must be taken as illustrations of the efforts of many thousands of staff and volunteers who have helped make the RD&E what it is today.

A building is only a shell for the people and the activities which it houses. Today's people have their stories which are yet to be told.

Fifty years after the beginning of the NHS, Exeter has a superb hospital building, outstanding staff and an unrivalled tradition. An illustrated sheet sold to raise funds for the hospital at a Fancy Bazaar on Northernhay, 31 July–1 August 1849, expresses sentiments which ring just as true today:

Where pain finds refuge, - Mis'ry dries her tears…
There pining sickness may in peace recline
Whilst godlike Science lends its aid divine…
Devonians glory in these works of love
Which find their recompense in realms above.

KEY DATES

1 January 1743
First patients admitted in Southernhay

1808
West of England Eye Infirmary founded

1899
The Devon & Exeter Hospital added 'Royal' to its name

1905
New Infirmary at the Workhouse

1927
Princess Elizabeth Orthopaedic Hospital opened

5 July 1948
National Health Service began

1959
Maternity Unit open at City Hospital

30 June 1966
Pathology and Public Health laboratories opened

1 April 1974
Area Health Authorities set up

8 July 1974
First patients admitted at Wonford

31 March 1982
Area Health Authorities shut down

1984
Decision that Wonford must be demolished and replaced

June 1992
First patients admitted to the new hospital

October 1992
West of England Eye Infirmary transfers to new RD&E

1 April 1993
RD&E became an NHS Trust

October 1997
First patients admitted to the new Princess Elizabeth Orthopaedic Centre

APPENDIX

Nurses' League Magazine 1971.

Progress with the Salmon Structure and Items of Interest.

The Chief Nursing Officer (CNO 10) is Miss A. F. Hutchinson as stated in the last magazine. She is in charge of all the Nursing Services of the hospitals which come under the Exeter and Mid-Devon Hospital Management Committee. Her office is at 26, Queen Street where the HM. offices are – she will eventually move to the new Wonford Hospital when it opens in 1973.

Principal Nursing Officer (PNO 9) of the General Division is Miss J. Norfolk who was appointed to this post in August, 1970. Before this she was the first Assistant Matron of the Royal Devon and Exeter Hospital, Southernhay. At the moment she is based at the Princess Elizabeth Orthopaedic Hospital.

Principal Nursing Officer (PNO 9) of the Teaching Division is Miss M. Brown who until August, 1970 was the Principal Nurse Tutor. Miss Brown is 'Head of Nurse Training' and responsible for the Group School of Nursing (Students and Pupils).

Senior Nursing Officer (SNO 8) General Division. There has been no appointment made yet for this post.

Senior Nursing Officer (SNO 8) Geriatric Division. This is Mrs V. M. Hooper who was Matron of Redhills Hospital. She is working from the Heavitree branch.

Senior Nursing Officer (SNO 8) Teaching Division. This is Miss E. J. Ashe who was the Senior Nurse Tutor. She is responsible for the Student Nurse Section.

Student nurses May 1973

The second post of SNO 8 of the Teaching Division is vacant at the moment. This person will be responsible for the pupil nurses and also for those training at the Princess Elizabeth Orthopaedic Hospital. Miss A. Barter, Miss Sandell and Miss M. Staddon (who also acts as Home Sister) are looking after the Southernhay branch. Miss B. Hayman is responsible for the West of England Eye Infirmary. Miss Clark, Miss Cox and Miss Tozer are looking after the Heavitree branch of the Royal Devon and Exeter. They must be eagerly looking forward to the opening of the new hospital block which is to be this Autumn. The dining room is already in use and also the changing rooms which have 'showers' and very nice sitting rooms adjoining.

Nurses' League Magazine 1972

Further progress with the Salmon Structure.

Since the printing of the magazine last year many of the senior nursing staff of the Exeter Hospitals have been appointed into the Salmon Structure, with only a few posts being advertised nationally.

As you know, the Chief Nursing Officer and the Principal Nursing Officer has been in the post for nearly two years; the Senior Nursing Officer for just over one year.

Last year – 1971 – a Senior Nursing Officer (No 8) for the new Wonford Hospital was appointed, as also were many Nursing Officers (No 7's) for the Exeter Hospitals.

Senior Nursing officer for Wonford
This is Mrs Hales, who is to have the day-to-day responsibility of this new hospital. At the moment she is "commissioning", or in other words Mrs Hales is getting ready for the "big move" in the near future, making sure that there will be smooth running as soon as it is opened.

Nursing Officer Appointments
The senior staff interested in these posts applied for the areas in which they were interested. The area that the No 7 is responsible for is called a 'Unit'; this consists of several wards or of several departments.

Royal Devon and Exeter Hospitals

Southernhay
Miss A. Barter has the Medical Unit and so is responsible for the following wards: Creswell, Newcourt, and Elizabeth, and this also includes the Isolation Unit. She also 'acts up' for Southernhay branch when the Senior Nursing Officer (Mrs Hooper) is off duty.
Miss M. M. Sandell has the remaining wards of this hospital, representing the Surgical Unit.
Miss S. Carpenter has the responsibility of several departments – the Accident and Emergency, Out-patients, and the Intensive Care Unit.
Miss P. Mogg is No 7 for the theatres.
Miss E. B. Raphael is now the Nursing Officer on night duty.

Heavitree
Miss M. Clarke is the Nursing Officer for the Geriatric Unit and also for Newcourt Hospital.
Miss P. Cox has the responsibility of the main surgical and medical wards; these are the wards in the new block, and when it is fully opened it will include the gynaecological ward and a large children's ward.
Mr. R. Ions is now the night duty No. 7 for this branch. He was, until December 31st, 1971, the Charge Nurse of Sheldon Ward (Southernhay).

Paediatric Unit
Miss Timms, who has come from Carshalton, Surrey, has this unit, which consists of the children's wards of the Southernhay and Heavitree branches and also Honeylands.

West of England Eye Infirmary
Miss B. Hayman is responsible for this unit.

Whipton Hospital
This hospital has the medical ward, two geriatric wards and the Renal Dialysis Unit. Mr L. Hardy is the Nursing Officer for this Unit.

The Princess Elizabeth Orthopaedic Hospital
Miss Born and Miss Perring have the divided responsibility of this hospital.

Redhills and Ernsborough House (Geriatric)
This is divided into two units. Miss D. Hermitage has Ernsborough House and a few wards at Redhills. Miss K. Radford has the remaining wards at Redhills and also the day ward.

The Peripatetic Nursing Officers
'Peripatetic' is described in the dictionary as 'walking about'. This is the duty of Mrs B. Raw and Miss Tozer. They relieve during holidays of other Nursing Officers, so they should certainly know all the Exeter Hospitals very well by now.
Miss M. Staddon and Miss Hunt both share

the work of looking after all the students and pupils. This means a lot of rushing from one hospital to another.

The Nursing Officers are responsible for the day-to-day running of their units and report to the Senior Nursing Officer. Each unit has a meeting about once a month, the Nursing Officer acting as chairman, as the Matron used to at sister's meetings. If a Ward Sister or Charge Nurse cannot attend the unit meeting then her/his Staff Nurse does. A member of the School of Nursing is also allo-

cated to a unit and so attends its meetings. The Nursing Officer does daily rounds of the patients and is there to help and advise any of the nursing staff in that unit. The Ward Sisters also take it in turn to "act up" when their No 7 is off duty. All the Nursing Officers of an area have frequent meetings with the Senior Nursing Officer and Principal Nursing Officer. The Principal Nursing Officer and the Senior Nursing Officers, with the equivalent from the teaching area, also meet with the Chief Nursing Officer about once a week.

ACKNOWLEDGMENTS

The earlier history of the Royal Devon & Exeter (RD&E) has been told in two books: J. Delpratt Harris, *The Royal Devon and Exeter Hospital* (1922) and P.M.G. Russell, *A History of the Exeter Hospitals 1170–1948* (1976). The latter includes a section on the history of the Eye Infirmary, which has also been described in greater detail by G.L. Cantrell, *West of England Eye Infirmary Exeter 1808–1992* (1992). The Princess Elizabeth Orthopaedic Hospital is portrayed from the viewpoint of a child patient in Rosemary Sutcliff's *Blue Remembered Hills* (1983).

On retiring, Dr Anthony Daly embarked on a history of the RD&E 1948–78 and interviewed many of his colleagues. He has generously lent me the fruits of his research. Since much of it would now have been irretrievable I have drawn deeply and gratefully on Dr Daly's files, to the extent that he should perhaps be acknowledged as co-author of the present work. I am also indebted to those who supplied Dr Daly with information in the 1980s, and those who patiently explained their areas of expertise in 1997. My sincere gratitude to (in alphabetical order):- Dr N.S. Alcock; Mrs Sheila Barnard; Miss Anne Barter; Miss Betty Biggs (Mrs Lauder); Miss Anne Branscombe; Prof. F.S.W. Brimblecombe; Mr Tony Bulgin; Mr K.P.S. Caldwell; Dr Alick Cameron; Mr A.L. Candler; Mr George Cantrell; Miss Elsa Batstone (Mrs Capener); Dr B. Chudecki; Mr John Churchill; Dr Brian Clarkson; Mrs Norah Clarkson; Mrs Julie Cotton; Dr Michael Dawrant; Mrs J. Dendy Moore; Mr F.C. Durbin; Dr. J.O.P. Edgcumbe; Dr K. Forbes; Mrs Elsie Fordham; Mr Murray French; Ms Angela Frost; Miss Ruth Furze; Mr A.C. Gairdner; Miss H. Graveney; Dr D.J. Pereira Gray; Mr J.L. Griffith; Dr R. Hadden; Mrs Monica Hadden; Dr T. Hargreaves; Cllr. Jack Harris; Mr David Harvey; Prof. Ruth Hawker; Mrs J. Hinde; Mr & Mrs G. Hingston; Miss Hodges (Mrs Hoby); Miss Jean Hurford; Mr M. Huscroft; Mr Derek Jefferiss; Mr C Jeffery; Miss Ruth Kelly; Miss Nona Kerslake; Mr David Knowles; Miss Jean Leiper; Ms Iris Mackie; Mrs Peggy Marshall; Prof. D. Mattingly; Sir Robin Maxwell-Hyslop; Dr Brendan Moore; Mrs Moyra Mucklow; Mgr M.P. O'Neill; Miss Rosemary Paget (Mrs Langman) Dr A.D. Perrett; Sir Desmond Pond; Mrs Hazel Poppleton; Dr K.J. Powell; Mrs A. Pribergs; Miss Beryl Raphael; Dr Adrian Rogers; Revd E. Royle; Mr P.M.G. Russell; Mr F.J. Rutter; Revd Dr John Searle; Mr Philip Scott; Dr C. Seward; Dr J.H. Simpson; Dr J.R. Simpson; Mr M.J. Soper; Mr Jack Sparrow; Dr G. Steele Perkins; Ms Val Trower; Mr Dick Venn; Mr Keith Vowles; Mr Nigel Walsh; Dr W.P. Walter; Dr Peter Warren; Dr Peter Watts; Ms Janet Wiles; Ms R. Windeatt; Mr Michael Woollacott.

INDEX

Figure in italics refers to illustrations

PICTURE CREDITS

The following kindly supplied etchings, postcards and photographs:

George Cantrell 12
Tony Daly 21, 22, 33, 35, 45, 47, 49, 60, 61, 80
Devon and Exeter Institution 14, 16
Monica Hadden 46, 53
Hazel Harvey 52, 62, 70
Nona Kerslake 43, 88
John Melville 81, 83, 84, 85
Mark Rattenbury 81, 83, 85
Nigel Walsh 6, 77, 79, 90
Westcountry Studies Library 11

All the other illustrations were supplied by the RD&E Healthcare Trust